Stories of Conflict and Passion

Derek Peters

David Pettigrew is a Belfast sculptor and a past President of the Ulster Arts Club.

Cover Illustration Natasha King.

This work is available on audio tape - Reader Tony King.

Other publications

Memories of a Sea Gipsy

Arc Publications £5.99. An account of life as a Radio Officer in the British, Greek and Norwegian Merchant Navies in the fifties. *"In particular, I enjoyed the way in which he describes the oddball characters with whom he found himself shipmates"*

- Sam McAughtry writer and broadcaster.
"Lively interesting amusing and vivid record"
- Telegraph
"Compelling reading".
I.S.N.

Contents

The Legacy

I sat in Belfast's Legion Club in Waring Street one Sunday morning savouring a pint of Guinness to restore my nervous system after the ravages of the Saturday night carousal. This was in the fifties when to get a drink on a Sunday was a privilege reserved for golfers and the more gregarious of the working class who had the foresight to join the Legion or the Buffs club or something of the sort. I was there because of my membership of what was pleased to be called the Merchant Navy which was still held in some esteem in those days. The reality was of course that I worked on a ship owned by capitalist who was in it for the profit. Still and withal, my merchant seaman's discharge book entitled me to use the bar facilities of the British Legion as if I was a war hero.

I shared the porter-stained table with two midde-aged working men who were lingering over the remains of two pints of single x, as the weaker stout or porter was then known. The floor waiter passed the table. I ordered another pint to keep the other one company. One of the men held up his pint glass with half and inch of stout at the bottom.

"Put a top of that, old hand",

he said to the waiter in the tone of a valued customer dispensing largesse. The waiter said,

"Away to hell out of that, you spent all your money in Mosey Hunter's last night and now your lookin' free drink in the Legion this morning and the pair of you never served a day in your life."

I was feeling expansive and still had a good few pounds from my pay-off from the last ship so I said to the waiter,

"Make that three pints of single."

The two topers nodded in my direction and said I was a gentleman and with unerring accuracy asked me if I was 'on the boats'. In their experience the only people who had money to throw around on a Sunday morning were merchant seamen home on leave. They lifted their pints, nodded in my direction, said cheers and then ignored me to continue their conversation.

"He done the bag you know. That's how he got the sack from the trams."

They continued to talk about their mutual aquaintance who apparently was a tramcar conductor with the then Belfast Corporation Transport Department and had defalcated with the day's takings, which in those days were collected in a stout leather bag which hung round the shoulder of the conductor.

This brought back memories of a former aquaintance of my youth who was rather a free spirit for the times. John Gouk worked in the shipyard as a red leader, that is he applied red lead to the metal of the ship's hull. His occupation caused some consternation in the American consulate in Belfast some time later when applying for a visa to visit the US enroute to see his relatives in Canada. The US consul, obsessed with anti-communism, thought John was a real live red leader as in Fidel Castro and asked him to come to the consulate where no doubt he was finger printed and photographed before they realised he was a brush hand in the Belfast shipyard.

John was six foot tall, well built and black haired with large brown eyes and a protruding lower lip. He lived alone on account of his mother and brothers emigrating to Canada when he was twenty-one. He was now thirty-one and still lived in the kitchen house on the Newtownards Road where he had been born. He worked hard all week and anybody who knows about ships will tell you that lying on your back painting out a ships bilge with the rust and paint falling into your mouth is hard work indeed. John was also a very well read man, this being before the onslaught of television on people's minds. He loved poetry, especially of the activity tendency. He could recite, and often did in his cups, yards of 'Black Bess', 'Tam O'Shanter' and 'The Cremation of Dan Magee'. The reason John was so literate was simple; he was obliged to stay in the house Monday to Friday as all his wages were spent at the weekend. He had an arrangement with the woman next door, who would fetch in his groceries and coal from the Co-Op. First thing after work on a Friday night he would pay her thirty shillings for his Co-Op account and she could keep the dividend. For the next two days in his own eyes he lived like a king. John would boil the kettle, fetch out the zinc bath and scrub dirt, oil and rust flakes from his body. Then he would shave, put on fresh underwear and shirt, don his three piece worsted suit from the Co-Op in York Street, the cost of which the good neighbour woman paid by the week.

John Gouk's tiny kitchen boasted one armchair and a radio. The rest of the space was taken up with piles of books. There were books on art, books on history, books on the American wild west. There was even a book on mountaineering in the Himalayas even though John had never seen a mountain, except Slieve Donard through the window of McGinn's bar in Newcastle, County Down. Next John would place the frying pan on the gas stove while he listened to the news of the Northern Ireland Home Service as it then was. Those were in the days when the BBC was fair and objective and not the green parrot it has now become. He fried bacon, eggs, potato and soda bread with kidneys, liver and sausages and washed them down with a pint of hot strong sweet tea. This dish, now known as an Ulster fry, was John Gouk's diet and probably did him no harm as he burned off the excess calories at work. At any rate he dearly loved his fry and saw no reason the change it except at the end of the week when the stores were running low and he made do with boiled potatoes and margarine. There was a radio serial in those days called 'The McCooey's' which was listened to avidly by most of the population. John would put aside his greasy plate, stuff a cindery curly pipe with thick tarry tobacco, stretch his legs and puff away while he involved himself with the doings of the McCooeys.

It was a short walk from John's house to the "Vulkan Bar" which by this time was populated with the stragglers from the straight-from-work drinkers from the shipyard. They were always the same Friday night crowd, still in their dungarees, maudlin drunk on an empty stomach, ready to collapse about nine o'clock when they would be bundled out to make room for the night time regulars.

"Have you a licence for that thing? You should take that thing to Korea, the war would be over in no time."

John's pipe was always the subject of some mild ribbing and indeed he would have been disappointed if his presence was not observed. Two quiet pints of double and down the road to the "Great Eastern", called after the ship, as befitted a shipyard pub. Three pints there and a conversation with an old friend about the characters of Bobby Greer the grocer and Derek the window cleaner out of the McCooeys and John would be ready to move on down to the "Farmer's Rest", called as it was because it lay enroute from the farming country in the Castlereagh hills to the city markets.

John's progress could always be charted citywards from here on in, as he would always endeavour to be in the vicinity of a city centre drinking club where he would be persona grata at ten o'clock closing time. This could be one of the few respectable working men's clubs such as the Tramwaymen's, the Engineer's, the British Legion or the grandly named Ancient Order of

Buffaloes. He was always sure of a drink after hours at any of these bars. As I mentioned, all John's family took off for Canada where they had numerous relatives. One of these had been a tram conductor in Toronto all his days. He was a fractious man who lived on his own and had quarrelled with his relatives in Canada, which explains why, when he died, he left his money to his nephew John Gouk whom he had never seen. John had heard of him of course and his house was mentioned as a place of abode for him if he decided to emigrate, which he didn't. So it was an agreeable surprise when John opened the envelope with the Canadian stamp to find enclosed a solicitor's letter with a cheque for five hundred dollars from the Bank of Nova Scotia. John naturally didn't go to work that Friday morning but was waiting at the door of the bank for the staff to arrive. The clerk advised him to open an account thus earning interest on his two hundred and thirty pounds. The clerk had just finished filling in the requisite forms and had entered the amount in the new account.

"Wait a second, there are a few things I need to buy, I could do with some new duds and a new pair of shoes. You'd better give me ten pounds back."

The bank clerk was visibly irritated.

"I wish you would make up your mind."

John who was reluctant to part with his cash in the first place was visibly angered.

"You needn't bother your arse changing it. Give me it all back."

The clerk's apologies were to no avail. John scooped up the two hundred and thirty pounds and stalked off to the "Ulster Arms" in his dudgeon.

This, in Belfast's Templemore Avenue, was the start of John Gouk's peregrinations. Then followed a sort of advance into the city centre that took in the 'Vulkan', the 'Great Eastern', the 'Aero Arms' with it's neon lit aeroplane sign, finishing up in the Ulster Sports Club in High Street for tea. John was always welcome; he never left without buying the barmen a drink and in the Sports Club, which was strictly members only, he was given an extra large steak even though meat was rationed at the time. Next, he made his way to Commercial Court off Donegall Street where he met the secretary of his union, the Transport and General Workers. This was a large bellied expansive man who in the cups was much given to bursting into song with a voice that quelled all conversation. This day however he was ensconced with a journalist and a high court judge who was wont to place his off-course bets with the proprietor, which was strictly illegal at the time. The journalist was a small tubby man who was very gregarious as long as the drinks kept coming in time to his consumption. If the journalist's glass was empty he would hold it up to the light and shout in peevish tones,

"The tide's out."

This night however he had no cause for complaint as John would shout above the din in the bar, "Shop! Shop!" and continue thus until he was served. The high court judge, who had a consuming interest in the shipping industry, listened raptly while John rattled off the names of the Cunarders and Union Castle boats built in the shipyard. He knew the tonnage, the length of time on the stocks and the type and horse power of the engines. The union secretary, who was getting bored, threw back his head and sang in a roaring baritone voice

"If I can help somebody. Then my living shall not be in vain."

The volume of his voice drowned all conversation causing the customers either to join in the chorus or to take long swallows of their drinks, to the great satisfaction of the landlord who made perfunctory and feeble pleas for the cessation of the singing.

Closing time came sharply at ten o'clock, the landlord shouting exhortations to leave as he gathered up the glasses. Outside the bar a large Jaguar car was parked. Without waiting to be asked John levered himself into the back seat as the judge opened the door.

"To the 'Tramwaymen's'. I'll get yiz all in,"

John said to the judge who found himself in the role of a taxi driver. In those days a car could proceed in a direct line to any point of the compass in Belfast without let or hindrance and in next to no time they were in Ann Street outside a Victorian building with the doors firmly shut. John pressed the bell and a doorman appeared poking his nose through two inches of aperture.

"Jasus John! Have you brought the lost tribe with you? I can't possibly let yiz all in."

John put his hand to his mouth in a conspiratorial whisper.

"This man here is a judge of the realm. You might never know when you would need him."

The doorman who had a conviction for GBH said,
"Come on in your honour,"
as he ushered to whole party into the stairwell. Sotto voce he said to John,
"I believe that's the same ould bastard that gave me the two months, but as
you say it's good to have a friend in court."
The Belfast Corporation Transport Department Social Club was supposed to
be for tram drivers and conductors who worked unsocial hours and needed
a drink after their shift and indeed there were one or two Belfast Corporation
employees on the premises. Most of the customers however were carousers
who were only getting into their stride when the closing time descended on
them as if the lights were going out all over Europe. Then there would be
panic attacks until somebody suggested the 'Trams' or the 'Accentric Club',
and indeed the Accentric was well named. In one corner of the 'Trams' that
night a much decorated ex-soldier and rugby player was arguing with a fat
Scottish school teacher about the merits of Kipling as a poet. The ex-soldier,
recognising the judge, shouted a greeting and insisted that he and his party
join the company.
"This fat Scottish bastard here says Kipling was a jingoistic imperialist. I say
he was the other ranks' champion. The scourge of the military establishment. Something like myself in fact. I did a fair bit of scourging. I once
clocked a Brigadier in the mess one night. Got placed under close arrest for
it. Didn't charge me though. I had more gongs than he had and it might have
looked like jealousy."
John in the meantime had been joined by a neighbour who was a tram conductor. In fact he was just off the last shift, was still dressed in his blue serge
uniform with the red piping and leather cuffs. In those days before the con-
cept of a neutral working environment it was permitted to wear war service
ribbons on a tramway man's uniform. Of these John's neighbour had five
which he referred to as his fruit cocktail. His cash bag and ticket machine
were still over his shoulder. He had called in for a quick beer before checking
in his cash and unused tickets to the office.
"This is Sam, a good friend and neighbour of mine,"
said John as the little non-descript conductor nodded to each of the party.
Sam was a low set mild little man of forty or so who worried about his bald
pate so he kept on his conductor's peaked hat.

"I've had a bit of a windfall today Sam, so don't worry about your shout. I'll cover for you," said John.

"Congratulations ould hand but I'm well able to stand my whack in any company,"

Sam replied, sounding a wee bit miffed at the suggestion that he was out of his depth. In fact Sam had only enough to buy one round of drinks for the party and that would have cleaned him out.

The judge and the ex-soldier began telling yarns about their service days giving Sam, who landed in Normandy with The Royal Ulster Rifles, the chance to tell his yarn about how he liberated the Gestapo Chief's wine cellar at Caen.

"Never lipped water for a month after it,"

he asserted. John now felt the urge to entertain the company with a rendition of Rabbie Burns' poem 'Tam O'Shanter'.

"Tam sat supping at the nappie getting foo and unco happy,"

he roared out, silencing all conversation in the club. The judge who considered himself an authority of Lallan Scots applauded enthusiastically, giving John the excuse to launch into another roaring rendition of 'Black Bess'.

"Watch out thon ould horse kicks all round it" said Sam, alluding to John's flailing arms which he used to give emplasis to his words.

Sam's turn to buy a round came and still smarting from John's slight he insisted that everyone should have a double. Too late he realised that his wallet would not cover the amount required so he succumbed to the tram conductor's age-old temptation. He fished into the cash bag to finger four serrated edges that signified four half crowns.

The tubby journalist was tunelessly singing snatches of songs by Al Boley, a favourite jazz singer in the thirties. The judge, equally tuneless, was singing 'Bonnie Mary of Argyle', but as befitted a judge of the High Court demanded rapt attention. His attitude annoyed the war hero who did not suffer fools gladly. The war hero, who was six foot three, cleared a space, measured his length on the floor and began doing push ups, snorting through his nose like a boxer. The bar steward spotted a familiar train of events which usually ended in trouble.

"Circle the wagons Billy",

he said this to the doorman who responded by shouting, "Time gentlemen please. The police are on their way."

Indeed the police station was just across the road and if they were on their way they were on their way to get a drink after hours. John Gouk was panic stricken. He had a roll of notes in his pocket fit to choke a donkey and nowhere to get another drink.

"Why don't you get the new plane to Dublin John?" the barman said. That week a midnight flight to Dublin was inaugurated. It only took an hour against the two and a half hour journey by train.

"Indeed and why not. I can afford it now and besides that a pint of stout in Dublin is only one and three."

A pint of stout in Belfast cost one shilling and eleven pence in the old money at the time.

The barman said he would ring for a taxi to take John and Sam, whose bag by this time was well and truly done, to Nutt's Corner airport. The judge's Jaguar and the war hero's MG collided outside the club causing the police guard at the barracks to investigate. The whole party were arrested except John and Sam who got away in their taxi. When the Sergeant on duty found out the identities of his charges he had them all ferried home by a police driver who had to listen to Al Boley's greatest hits and 'Annie Laurie' until two o'clock in the morning when he dropped off the journalist and the judge on the Lisburn Road.

John Gouk and Sam arrived at the airport just in time to see the plane take off and head south. They persuaded the taxi man, who was expected home at half twelve, to drive them to Dublin for seven pounds. He insisted on seeing the money before he agreed. John went through his whole repertoire of Robert Service before he fell into the arms of Morpheus.

Sam, who was still sober, contemplated his position. The bag was well and truly 'done' now. He might as well be hung for a sheep as a lamb so he relaxed as he listened to his neighbour John Gouk's snores. Sam, like John, was a batchelor who lived on his own so there was no one to fret saving, perhaps the officials of the Belfast Corporation Transport Department.

They arrived at the door of the Shelbourne Hotel which was the most exclusive and expensive hotel in Dublin at the time. It was in fact the only hotel in Dublin known to the taxi man. His passengers had never been in Dublin before and as far as John was concerned as long as it had a licence he was happy. John explained to the doorman who answered the bell that he had just flown in from America and Sam was his chauffeur. A pound tip convinced the night porter to hand over the key to a room with two beds. Another pound persuaded him to open the dispense bar, although it was three a.m. There was a visiting priest and his niece supping Remy Martin in the lounge. John insisted they have another and that the night porter have a large one, which he did. Sam's uniform, ticket machine and bag were unfamiliar so he explained that he was a chauffeur attached to the British Embassy. He pointed to his medal ribbons to prove his point. He explained that his bag was a diplomatic pouch and his ticket puncher was a wireless transmitter direct to the Foreign Office.

Soon John was declaiming with his usual gusto.

"There's a one eyed yellow idol to the north of Katmandu. There's a little marble cross beneath the town. And a broken hearted woman tends the grave of Mad Carew. While the yellow god forever gazes down."

The recitation stirred the priest to exclaim,

"Great gas these Northern fellows."

"How do you remember the words?"

trilled his niece. This encouragement lead to "Gunga Din" and in fact a few more barrack room ballads and many more rounds of Remy Martin until the priest and Sam succumbed to sleep while the niece was on John's knee in rapt attention while the night porter was much richer. The morning found the priest in his own bed and John in the niece's, who in fact if the truth be told, was nobody's niece but that's a story for another day.

Sam awoke in the bedroom they had booked, scratched in his bag, found it empty so he went to look for John. Used as he was to shouting out the tramstops he went along the corridors shouting,

"John Gouk come out! John Gouk come out!"

A strange awakening indeed for the guests of the Shelbourne. It was a strange awakening too for the "priest's niece".

"Jasus I'd better get back to his bedroom or I'll be kilt."

With these words she skipped out of the bed and that was the last John ever saw of her. However, always a man to take the strange exigencies of life in his stride he lit his pipe and then shouted to Sam to sop his guldering and go down to breakfast.

The Georgian spendour of the Shelbourne Hotel had often seen dishevelled and hungover revellers but usually they were from the upper class rugby or show jumping fraternity. John's eyes were bloodshot, his hair askew, his shirt grubby and his dark strong stubble looked like three days growth. Sam, old soldier that he was, had washed his face and arranged what hair he had left over his bald pate. He had abandoned his cash bag and ticket punch in the room and only hoped that John's windfall was still intact. The head waiter, with the air of a man who had seen it all before, approached the pair at their table.

"What room number do you gentlemen have?"

He had been confident that a well rehearsed routine would have the pair fired out onto the steps.

"The very man I wanted to see,"

said John in loud commanding tones as he pressed a pound note into the head waiter's hand.

"Bring me and my friend here two Remy Martins with a raw egg in each and then we will talk about breakfast."

The head waiter instantly forgot about room numbers and scurried away to the bar. He recognised a roughness of money when he saw it.

"Two Bombay oysters gentlemen and your very good health",

he said as he pocketed the change and summoned a waitress with a snap of his fingers.

"First port of call for you and me, ould hand, is a barber's for a shave and a haircut and then we explore this town",

said John as he marched with belching pipe down Grafton Street with Sam hopping and running to keep apace. Ablutions over they found their way with unerring instinct to the 'Bailey' off Grafton Street which was just opening for business. A solitary middle-aged barman was polishing the glasses while a large fresh-faced man in a kilt was talking on the phone. The man was youngish, had a thick mop of blond hair and was bellowing down the phone in a cut-glass accent.

"Come down here at once Deirdre of I'll kill myself."

"Not in this fucken bar you won't", muttered the barman.

John liked a bit of a drama in a place. He also like the barman's approach to life.

"We get all sorts in here. Culchies up for the match, toffs like your man in the kilt, ordinary five eights, writers, con artists and piss artists of every discription."

John warmed to the place even more.

"I spread red lead on the arses of boats myself so I suppose you could call me a five eight. My mucker here works on the trams."

Sam took a bow and said,

"I suppose you could say I used to work on the trams but I done the bag last night so I expect I'll be on the dole when I get back."

The sympathetic barman pulled two pints of Guinness on the house. By lunch time John and Sam were restored to their normal good spirits, the kilty had decided not to kill himself but phoned another girl who seemed to give satisfactory responses.

A fat tousel-haired man sailed through the door with coat tails and shirt tails flapping. He was in his thirties, had the remnants of good looks and seemed well enough known to get credit from the barman.

"Tell the boss I'll settle later",

he said as he swallowed a pint of Guinness in two gulps and ordered another one. Observing Sam's uniform he asked if they were now running trams from Belfast to Dublin. He also informed the world in general that he had painted the Donaghadee lighthouse and alluding to Sam's service ribbons he said his brother Rory had fought through the war in the Royal Irish Fusiliers, the only regiment with it's motto in Irish. Apparently Rory was his half brother.

"I, myself, don't hold with armies",

he continued,

"I believe the pen is mightier than the sword although I've wielded both in my time."

The fat man kept up a sort of running philosophy lesson aimed at the world in general until and elderly tall lugubrious man appeared in the doorway.

"Aha!" the fat man shouted.

"The Monaghan wanker strikes again."

He kept up a stream of scatalogical abuse until the older man left the bar much to the amusement of the cognescenti. However John and Sam were utterly bemused. The fat man apparently having scored some sort of verbal victory invited John and Sam to accompany him to the back door of Neary's for something called the holy hour. It was explained to them that the pubs in Dublin closed for an hour after lunchtime so they let themselves be guided to the backdoor of a nearby Victorian pub where there was a crowd of earnest drinkers, both male and female. Their guide explained to them that these people were all theatricals and their admirers. He also explained to them that his credit was temporarily stopped in this establishment and that he would be obliged to his new Belfast friends if they could do the honours. John Gouk, nothing if not generous, willingly obliged and the fat man ordered a double Remy Martin. They were joined by a small bald elderly man with large blue eyes who said he was on the boards in Belfast. John and Sam were elated to meet a well known comedian who often graced the stage of the Opera House and the Empire Theatre and of course his health had to the drunk.

Lunch, in the form of hot meat pies, was supplied by the considerate staff of Neary's. The fat man was holding forth on every subject under the sun, applauding the victories of the People's Liberation Army in China and deploring the intervention of the US in Korea. John could see the barman's visage darkening. The fat man noticed it too.

"When Mao Tse Tung gets here don't you worry Sean. You will still be pulling pints but he'll put a halt to ould Bishop John Charles' gallop,"
he said.

"I'll not stand here and hear my Bishop insulted,"
said a small man with a pioneer pin in his lapel. He was drinking lemonade.

"Then sit down then and hear him being insulted, ye craw thumping sober guts,"
retorted the fat man.

John Gouk knew a row brewing up when he smelt it so he took charge of the situation by bellowing out the first verse of 'Dangerous Dan McGrew',
"A bunch of the boys were whooping it up in the Malamute saloon",
he declaimed, his voice drowning out all conversation. The actors of course deferred to the man on stage while they searched their minds for a monologue that topped John's performance. The little bald comedian was first off

the mark with the first line of 'Biddy Mulligan the price of the Coomb' vented before the last syllable of 'Dan McGrew' had died away. Thus a fierce ideological dispute was quelled by the natural tendency to upstage on the part of the thespians.

"Time we were out of this paddy whackery stage Irish craphouse,"

the fat man said. He led his two new friends down along the St Stephens Green past the Shelbourne where the fat man was refused admittance because of some past unspeakable misdemeanour, according to the doorman. They continued on the Merrion Row where a fine Victorian bar stood on the corner.

"Let's go down to Ryan's or Foley's for a bit of a wet",

quoted the fat man from O'Casey.

"I don't know about Foley's but this is Ryan's".

It was now five pm and the long brassed bar was filling up with earnest myopic young men sporting golden ring badges. They all seemed to favour blue suits with grey or Fair Isle pullovers. They all seemed to be afflicted with acne.

"This must be a sailor's bar. They are all talking Dutch,"

whispered Sam.

"Not at all",

maintained John "they are all Italians. Don't I hear it all the time in Forte's chippy on the Albertbridge Road. This is probably the Italian watering hole in Dublin".

Their curiousity was assuaged by the fat man who said in a loud voice that he had got lost in Rome one time and had asked a priest the way home. The priest had asked him how he knew that he could speak English. He had answered that the spotted he was wearing a Fainne which is the golden ring Irish speakers wear. The myopic young men glared at him. The fat man asserted that he spoke better Irish than any of them, in Irish.

"Tell me",

said the fat man to the tall elderly and solemn proprietor who wore the traditional barman's canvas apron and a white shirt with a starched collar and tie.

"In all these years serving these Gaelic league officials from their next door office, did you ever learn any Irish yourself?"

The elderly proprietor thought for a moment and then said
"Yes, 'airgead sios', money down."
Sam however was beginning to feel uncomfortable because his uniform and
medal ribbons were obviously the subject of some discussions among the
Gaelic speakers. The fat man said in a loud voice
"And you tell me you fly all over the world with B.O.A.C."
The muttering among the Gaelic speakers ceased. Many rounds later the trio
found themselves outside the door of Doheny and Nesbitt's pub, it being
closing time. The fat man who had a thirst as prodigeious as John's guided
them to a Georgian house nearby.
"You may have heard of the United Arts Club, well this is the disunited Arts
Club. The one prerequisite for admission is that you be barred from the
United Arts Club."
The fat man led the way down some steps into the basement. The man who
answered the doorbell had a black trilby hat on the back of his head and a
glass of whiskey in his hand. He was dressed entirely in black and also
sported dark glasses. Inside, men and women sat around a turf fire in an
elegant Georgian grate.
The tall lugubrious man who was traduced in the 'Bailey' earlier was there
but the fat man made no effort of acknowledge him. John instinctively knew
the reason. If he was shagged out of the cellar at this time he would get no
more drink until the pubs opened in the morning. The man in black, who said
he was a civil servant, said to John in a mocking way,
"You'll be up for the match then. A bogball follower or it it stickball? One of
these County Down supporters with 'Up Down' on their hats."
"What in the name of Jasus are you talking about? I support Glentoran if I
support any of them."
"Never mind him he's just trying out lines for his next book. It'll be in Irish
at the taxpayers expense and the Department of Education will pay him to
translate it find out what it is all about."
The fat man had an unerring feel for the jugular.
Groups of strange people stood around arguing the toss. Actors with faces
still caked in cosmetics declaimed in stentorian tones. Writers disputed the
meaning of 'Ulysses' with Jesuititcal ingenuity. However they all had the one

thing in common with John and Sam. They were all fond of a drink as the Irish understatement goes.

Sam fell asleep in easy chairs. Other topers paired off into gloomy ante rooms with long-skirted poetesses.

Dawn came with John and the fat man still supping neat whiskey from cracked cups. Sam had succumbed to sleep and various somnolent bodies lay stretched around the place. The fat man surveyed the scene and expressed disgust at the lack of stamina of the middle classes.

"To the markets my old friend, if the readies are still holding out".

His remarks were directed to John as he had observed that Sam's conductor's bag had long since emptied. Sam was roused and the trio made their unsteady way across O'Connell Bridge and down the quays. They came to a decrepit pub in a cul-de-sac beside the vegetable market. It boasted an early licence to satisfy the thirsty produce carters after their long drive up from the country. It was already seven o'clock so they gained admittance along with a very tall stooped man with a long nose and a formidable beer gut.

"Aha! Fat man", he said.

"I would gather you have not yet been to bed unlike myself who has slept for seven hours. But do you know that sleep does not really refresh you. After a few pints, you know I don't partake of spirits, you go to sleep but your brain doesnt sleep. Your conscious mind does be argufying with your subconscious mind and that's why you wake up bolloxed".

"Of course", said the fat man.

"It's nothing at all to do with the sixty pints you drank during the day. I always knew that. The headaches were put destroying a man's happiness".

The bar curate intervened to inform the tall man that he was wanted on the phone.

"Some culchie trying to sell him a load of cabbages",

said the fat man.

"Is it true that he would drink sixty pints in a day?"

said John.

"Yes he is a produce dealer and the pub is his office from seven in the morning to lunch time. The rest of the day is recreational or social drinking."

John was impressed. Sam had fallen asleep again.

The fat man returned to air a beef about the inconsiderate nature of the Dublin Corporation.

"Do you know that I was on my way home from here last week with forty or fifty pints on boards when I stopped to have a leak. I nearly always stop at the same place at the corner where the old 'Home and Colonial Stores' used to be. I put my hand out to steady myself against the wall and wasn't the Corporation after knocking the building down and I fell over and peed all over myself. Most inconsiderate."

A consensus of agreement was supplied and the tall man ordered pints all round. An infant came into the bar with a quart jug.

"A quart of porter for me mammy,"

she said.

"There is an interesting story,"

the tall man said.

"The mammy was to play the Virgin Mary in the Corpus Christi procession and I was to guard the chapel the night before. The priest barred the mammy from the procession on account of her being a brass nail, so I found out where the alter wine was and drank the lot, just to teach the clergyman priest a bit of toleration"

said the fat man.

John Gouk felt a recitation coming on,

"On the Shankill Road a man named Groat. Had a wife who continually got his goat. Until one day he resolved to cut her scraggy throat."

"Fair play to him,"

commented the tall man.

"That's a bit extreme,"

said the fat man.

"I mean to say there's no call for extreme measures in Northern Ireland. They have civilized divorce there. Not like this benighted country. I intend to get married at some stage and will always refer to my wife as the first Mrs. to make her aware that nothing is forever."

"I don't expect I will ever marry,"

said the tall man.

"I mean to say, there are very few women come into the pub. Anyway I am fifty now and I am the first to admit that I am very set in my ways."

John continued his monologue, the story of which had the wife recovering from her cut throat, and the protagonist hanging himself with a sheet.
"The razor blade was German made and the sheet was Belfast linen,"
he continued.
Sam felt sorely in need of rest. The assault on Caen was easier than this he thought. Gouk must still have plenty of funds and the fat man obviously is a drinker in the Olympic class. The way to get John back to Belfast and he must get back before he drinks the ticket money, is to get him comatose.
Indeed John was in hardy company. The fat man was still coherent, even eloquent. The tall man, in between deals, would sink a pint in two gulps. Which of them wold be the first to throw in the towel? About lunchtime John felt another monologue coming on.
"Take me back to Mandolay. Where the flying fishes play. And the dawn comes up like thunder over China across the bay."
John's memory deserted him and his coherance slithered as his body did the same down the bar stool.
"Now that's a pity",
said the fat man.
"I don't like to see the proletariat letting down the side like that. The poor man must have a weakness somewhere. It's natures way of letting him know that. I once knew a man who was warned off the gargle. The poor man was forced to drink mild English beer for the rest of his life. Now that must have been a terrible cross the bear."
The tall man said this as he ordered the eighteenth round.
Sam saw his chance. He asked the potboy to order a taxi which duly arrived. The fat man and the produce dealer carried John into the back of the taxi as Sam searched for and found the remainder of the wad of notes. There was still a fair bundle, which only goes to show how the cost of living has gone up since then. He extracted enough to cover the rail fare and replaced them. They had no need to go to the hotel for the bag and the ticket machine. Sam's job was well and truly gone by this time.
The taxi driver helped carry John into Amien Street which was no easy task. The tickets were bought and as luck would have it a train was due to leave for Belfast. Sam breathed a silent prayer as the taxi driver and himself lowered John into a seat. He was still snoring heavily. The driver was tipped and

thanked and the train pulled out of the station. John awakened at Dundalk, the town just south of the border, as lawless then as it is now.

"Where the hell am I?"

he exclaimed.

"You're in Dundalk John, we're going home"

Sam told him. John thrust his hand into his breast pocket and felt the remains of his legacy.

"Indeed by Christ I'm not."

With this he sprang at the door, ran down the platform and disappeared. Sam arrived home to pick up his mail which included a letter from the Belfast Corporation Transport Department enclosing his employment cards and a request for the return of his bag and ticket machine. The letter did not mention the defalcation or restitution. The manager was experienced enough not to waste the typist's time.

John arrived home the next day. He was silent about his time in Dundalk but it was apparent that all the rest of the money was gone. His job was held for him in the shipyard and he got Sam started as a sheetmetal worker's helper. Sam did not like the shipyard. The cold east wind blowing down the Lough plus the fumes and noise were hard to stick. Eventually by dint of his war service, in those days ex-service men got preference, he got a job as an ambulance driver. John, as he lay on his back painting deck heads with the rust flakes and paint falling in his eyes and mouth, often felt a glow of satisfaction as he remembered the spending of his legacy.

The Witness

The Witness

The low hills to the south of County Tyrone make a pleasing background to what was Gary Johnstone's bungalow. The bungalow, of a type ubiquitous all over these islands now, had a quarter acre of rockery plant, shrubs and palm trees fronting the road. The driveway of standard tarmacadam led to an integral garage. What was different about Gary Johnstone's bungalow was the fact that it had bullet-proof glass and a security camera mounted over the door.

Gary Johnstone was a serving policeman in 1985 at the height of what the media is pleased to call The Troubles. Living so near the border with the Irish Republic he had taken every reasonable precaution he could to forestall an attack by the nationalist paramilitaries. Inside the house he had a panic button that activated an alarm in Clogher RUC barracks. His twenty-five year old wife and their three year old son were practiced in the drill necessary to secure the house and to summon help.

From the direction of Fintona two youths on a Honda motorbike were speeding towards the village of Clogher and Gary Johnstone's bungalow. They seemed to be in a carefree mood with scarves flying as they skimmed round the corners of the winding mountain road. At one stage an oncoming motorist had to take to the ditch as they flew past them. The motorist was shaken and angry enough to look in the back view mirror to try and catch the number of the bike. He glimpsed the letters EBZ before the motorbike disappeared from view round the next corner.

From the direction of Augher a Fiat 125 was being driven by a young woman in police uniform towards the village of Clogher and Gary's bungalow. This young woman was Jean Craig, Gary's sister-in-law. Police people, like the republicans they fight, tend to live a very restricted milieu and indeed it was through working alongside Jean that Gary met his future bride. It was a bright June night and Jean's shift at Augher police station had finished at seven. The hedges were in full bloom, with dark red fuschia alternating with white hawthorne. Jean's mind was on the circumstances that changed her life as a school teacher in a border three-teacher school to a police woman in a fortified barracks where the danger of a car bomb or mortar attack was ever present. The school had closed as the Protestant farmers close to the border had abandoned their small holdings to the relative safety of the towns and taken their children with them. Jean was a tall dark-haired woman with brown soulful eyes and a wide generous mouth showing perfect teeth when she smiled. Only a slightly elongated nose diminished her otherwise classical beauty. Jean had been one of the five hundred successful applicants out of two thousand who had applied for teacher training in her year. When she had finished her course she moved to the border school and when it closed her first thought had been to go to Scotland or England to continue her career. The thought of separation from her parents and friends had been too daunting so she opted for the police in order to stay at home. She considered that the terrorist compaign would have to end some time and then she would go back to teaching. That was four years ago and the terrorism continued with no counter strategy other than containment in place. There had been no great element of patriotism in her decision to join the Royal Ulster Constabulary. The pay was good, much more than she earned as a school teacher and there was the chance to mix with young active men who were thin on the ground in County Tyrone. The uniform flattered her and as she spent the greater part of her life wearing it that was important to her. As she settled into the new life she became aware that the terrorists, while calling themselves an army, were very quick to demand all the rights of a civilian when caught and a lot of the policemen were frustrated at seeing them every day at the normal peaceful mundane activities of life, like shopping in the supermarkets or drinking in the village pubs. She soon absorbed the police culture of trust withdrawal, of despising government ministers and officials and of disdain for the tattooed thugs who called themselves loyalist counter terrorists.

Then she had brought her sister along to a police function where her sister had met and soon married Gary Johnstone. This meant that they were now an extended police family.

Gary Johnstone was a six-foot two Viking of a man, an ex-lance sergeant in the Irish Guards who, on the expiry of his service, followed the well worn ex-guardsman's path to the RUC. He played rugby for the local team, had a carefree attitude to life and knew every rebel song in the book from his nights in the sergeant's mess in Chelsea Barracks. The rebel songs had stopped however when the terrorists had ambused the Irish Guards band and left the bandsmen writhing in agony on the tarmac of Green Park, London, their saffron kilts soaked in blood. He was thirty now with his whole life centred round his wife and baby son. The rugby club and the golf club, were the ringfenced limits of his relaxation. He had passed his sergeant's examination and it was only a matter of time when he would be promoted, hopefully to a less dangerous location where his wife and baby could be safe.

Gary drove his patrol car past the security gates at Clogher Barracks into the vehicle compound. He checked in his sub-machine-gun into the armoury, donned his civilian anorak and tweed cap, then drove his Volvo estate out of the barracks and on to the road towards his home. He was looking forward to the evening meal in the golf club and the shop gossip with his sister-in-law who was coming to babysit. He mused on the irony of his now dead parents grieving at his joining the army with its connotations or an early death when in all his ten years service he had never heard a shot fired in anger. Now here he was at home in Ulster in the police, which would have delighted his parents and the atmosphere was redolent of menace and death. He banished the morbidity from his mind and returned to the joyous aniticipation of the evenings prospect.

The two youths on the motorbike had skirted the village of Clogher by means of a by-road and were now ascending the mountain road towards the Johnstone's bungalow. The driver in high excitement recognised it as they passed it.

"That's it Pearse! That's where the fucker lives!"

He drove a hundred yards further up the road where they both dismounted. They were both long-haired, nondescript in appearance and dressed in the teenage uniform of denim jacket and jeans. They had forsaken their trainers for leather soled shoes because of the tread mark. Pearse was myopic with thick lensed glasses causing him to peer close to the zipper of the canvas bag he had under his jacket. He opened it to bring forth the metal parts and plastic butt of an armilite rifle. The driver said,

"Here give it me, I'll put it together,"

as he expertly joined up the innocent looking pipes to make up the sinister looking weapon.

The driver was Sean McManus, a student from a farming background with mousey hair, acne cratered skin, grey-green eyes and thin fuzzy moustache. Sean McManus and Pearse Gormley took up firing positions behind a hedge opposite the closed gates of Gary Johnstone's bungalow. They heard the sound of the Volvo diesel some ten minutes later as it rounded the last bend in the road before the bungalow. The two youths watched as Gary swung the Volvo into the driveway to halt at the gates. As he opened the door of the car to get out, the youth Sean McManus stood up from behind the low hedge to level the armalite at the back of Gary's head. He squeezed the trigger four times but the first shot had killed Gary stone dead. It had gone straight between his shoulder blades and out through his heart. The door of the bungalow opened. Irene, Gary's wife, rushed out fearing the worst and hoping for the best. Gary's heart had ceased to beat, the blood from multiple wounds were now spreading on the tarmac where he lay at the foot of the opened car door. In a paroxysm of shock all Irene could think to do was to press the panic button in the hall. She did this as Jean Craig's Fiat 125 rounded the bend. Jean could see the Volvo but as yet she could not see Gary's lifeless body but she could see Pearse Gormley packing his holdall with the armalite parts before he mounted the pillion seat. As the bike accelerated away the youth Gormley turned his head to see what was behind him. At that moment, at a distance of fifty yards in clear sunlight, WPC Craig got a full view of the nondescript youthful face framed in light brown hair and topped by the thick lensed spectacles.

Irene ran back to the living room and arched her body over the infant. She knew that Gary was dead and that what she had feared most had come to pass and her instinct was to protect her child. She had lived with the possibility of sudden death ever since she had given her heart to Gary and now it had happened and she just felt numb. The crumpled body between the car door and the seat was somehow not her husband. Her husband was always singing, laughing with her and at her and at himself. She clutched the boy to her bosom and rocked him backwards and forwards.

Jean Craig stopped, jumped from her car and ran to Gary's body, felt his pulse, realised he was dead and called her station on her personal radio. The constable on duty relayed the call to Clogher barracks to be told that the police with an army escort were racing to the scene having been alerted by Irene's panic button.

The sun was casting long shadows when the two assassins parked their motorbike in the garage of a safe house in Monaghan town, just over the Irish border. Later when they went to the pub known as the Bazooka Bar a cheer greeted their entrance. The news of the killing had reached the assorted sympathisers, guff republicans and IRA men on the run, who frequented the pub. The pair were feted and toasted on a successful operation and generally made to feel like heroes. The news announcer on radio four reported the killing as the fifth item on his report. As the pints of Guinness flowed Pearse Gormley raised his voice in song.

"Take it down from the mast Irish traitors
It's the flag we republicans claim
It can never belong to Free Staters
For they brought on it nothing but shame
Leave it to those who are willing
To uphold it in war or in peace
To those who intend to keep killing
Until England's tyranny cease."

He finished the song in an outburst of alcohol induced emotion while the gathering, their false consciousness rising to the heady brew, answered with a triumphal roar.

Sean McManus however did not join in the singing. He thought the song a piece of crude doggerel. He didn't like songs in English at the best of times as he was a Gaelic speaker who composed love poetry in that language. It did not bother him that he had murdered another human being but as a devout Catholic he was bothered from time to time as to whether he was engaged in constituted a just war in theological terms. His farmer father, who had served time for republican activities, had once said that you were not a real republican until you have done a peeler. Now he had done that and he was not sorry but he did not want to be caught and put in jail with a lot of riff-raff like the people who were roaring and bawling all round him at the moment. He wanted to finish his degree in Irish studies and hopefully get a job in broadcasting or if he was good enough to go on to do a P.hd. He had ideas too about the political end of it. He could see himself in the leadership of Sinn Fein where already he had the ear of the top man. He had heard the quotation from Lenin that the ability to combine legal activities with illegal activities was the mark of a true revolutionary. For Protestants he had unreserved hatred and contempt. As far as he was concerned they were interlopers and land grabbers who had no right to be in Ireland in the first place. The republican movement could cut a deal with the Brits because the Brits had no heart for the struggle.

The top man had listened to these ideas of his and that meant more to him than the approval of the lumpen rabble in the bar. Sean slipped out of the bar by the back door and made his way to the safe house where he slept soundly. Pearse Gormley on the other hand drank pint after pint of stout until he had slumped on the floor, when he was carried home by his admiring companions. Two uniformed Civic Guards watched from across the street, watched, but did nothing.

On the other side of the border a detective sergeant of the Ulster police started the procedure of a murder enquiry. The forensic man measured the trajectory of the bullets in Gary Johnstone's body, photographed the tyre tracks of the motorbike which was believed to have been stolen in Dungannon the previous day. Jean Craig gave the detective the description of the youth who was on the back of the motorbike and later in Clogher barracks she picked out the photograph from the book of terrorist suspects.

"That's him!" That's the bastard who turned around. About five-foot-seven with glasses like jam jar bottoms."

The rifling of the bullets extracted from Gary's body were found to match an armalite which had been used in other murders and murder attempts in the border area. Gary's widow, when she emerged from the tranquilliser-induced fog to face the anguish of reality was able to identify Pearse Gormley as the pillion rider.

The police picked up Pearse Gormley the following day when he went to sign for his unemployment benefit. He was still hung over from the previous night's carousal so the detective sergeant rushed him to the interrogation centre in Armagh straight away. His escort punched him in the ribs when he got him in the car. Gormley cried out in pain as the policeman seized his thick glasses and broke them in two. Gormley blinked his myopic grey eyes and tried to focus.

"You murdering fucking bastard! Gary Johnstone was a good friend of mine."

The policeman pummeled him with blows to the body.

"That's enough,"

the detective said.

"We have enough to send him down for life."

"I want him fucking dead."

The uniform man said as he tugged the handcuffs which bound him to Gormley.

Pearse Gormley winced as the cuffs dug into his flesh. His nerves were shattered and his stomach heaved with bile. He felt that he wanted to vomit and he was badly in need of a smoke. He thought about the various reports written by sympathetic lawyers and if only half of what they said was true about the interrogation centres, he was in for a rough time. He asked the driver to stop the car he was going to be sick.

"Hold his head out the window and let him boke,"
the detective said.

"I'm not stopping the car. You can hose it down when we get there."
Gormley vomited copiously out the window as the wind blew bits of his bile back in his face. He felt even worse.

"I'm dying for a smoke. Any chance of a fag?"
He asked the detective.

"The only fag you're getting is a lit one against your arse,"
the detective answered.

The uniform man laughed.

Gormley was brought straight away to the interview room where the arresting detective was joined by another interrogator. The other interrogator was a thickset grey haired man with his hair combed forward in the sixties style as if he still craved his youth now vanished. His head seemed to sit on his shoulders without any neck. His face was pleasant and his smile showed even well kept teeth. He was dressed in a freshly laundered crisp white shirt and expensive well cut jeans and mocasin style shoes. The first detective beside him looked shabby in a baggy suit and rumpled collar. Detective sergeant Sean Ramsey had been doing this job for twenty years and prided himself on knowing just how long it would take before the suspect broke. He regarded the nondescript wiry youth blinking in the flourescent light and gave him three days.

"You will want a solicitor. Flannagan and Meehan no doubt and I can tell you now what he will tell you. He will tell you to say nothing at all and to bump your eye on something on the seventh day and scream for a doctor. However, that may not be in your best interest as I will explain later. Anyway, there's the phone and that's his number."

Pearse Gormley rang the number to be told that a solicitor from that office would be on his way as soon as one came back from the courts. As soon as the youth put down the phone, John McKillop, the arresting detective, seized Gormley by his shirt collar, frog marched him into the toilet next door and thrust his head into the toilet bowl and pulled the chain. Pearse Gormley screamed after he vomited again and the water flushed the bile into his eyes, nose and mouth.

"I'll tell Mr Flannagan that you tortured me,"
Gormley cried.

"Don't think Flannagan will waste his time on the likes of you. He only comes for the top men. You are only cannon fodder. All you will get is a snotty nose apprentice who thinks he knows the law but knows fuck all. Now tell me who was with you on the motor bike or you will get the same again."
McKillop said.

"I don't know about any motor bike. I was in Moran's pub in Fintona all day Friday."
Gormley's voice was shaking as he answered. Then he remembered he was not supposed to say anything.

"Who mentioned Friday?"
McKillop said.

"Anyway we know it was you that murdered Gary Johnstone. We have a witness. What we want from you is the name of the driver. I will read you the names of all the cut throats in your gang and you will tell me which one it was."

McKillop's complexion indicated a fondness for liquor and his face had a five o'clock shadow at twelve o'clock. He had passed his forty fifth birthday and realised he would not get the promotion his wife so dearly wanted. His grey hair was thin on top and now his brow was beaded with sweat. A young solicitor arrived at that point from Flannagan and Meehan and the questioning stopped. The two detectives treated the lawyer disdainfully knowing he would relay what had been said back the to IRA.

The young lawyer told Gormley to say nothing at all and asked if he had incriminated himself in anyway. He told of the incident in the toilet which the lawyer duly noted for the trial. On his way out the detective sergeant formally informed the lawyer that the suspect had been sick in the car and had also vomited in the toilet. They duly recorded this on the video. Detective Sergeant Sean Ramsey then took over the interrogation:

"Pearse my son, I have been in this game a long time. I have put away a lot of boys like you, amadans mostly, but, they all finished up doing life because they wasted my time. Not that I mind the time because the more you stay mute the more overtime I can claim. I run a new BMW and it's guys like you pay for it. I have your record here Pearse and I see you beat up a young guy in a disco. You got fined and bound over for that. I see you got three months in the young offenders for vandalising a Church of Ireland hall. Bit of a tearaway. Just the sort of mad cap the provos use to do their dirty work. They won't do life. They make speeches."

Pearse Gormley felt his head swim. He wanted just to lie down and curl up. He was frightened that the man in the suit would physically abuse him but he was equally terrified that the man in jeans would draw him out. He realised that he must have been seen by the woman in the car and that all they wanted was the name of the driver. He just wished that they would let him go and that he could go over the border again to be stood drinks and treated like the hero he was. Detective Sergeant Ramsey lit a cigarette to taunt him and droned on. God how he wanted a smoke.

"I know your father you know. A decent man, hard working brickie, treasurer of the GAA Club. I once played against him when I was at college. All that had to stop when I joined the police, a pity really."

Ramsey mused.

"I know your father is no republican but he would be heart scalded if his son got the name of being a tout."

"I'm no tout"

Gormley blurted out before he could stop himself.

"Ha-ha, you know that and I know that but if we let you go and arrested the driver would the rest of the world know it?"

Sergeant Ramsey was warming to his theme.

"Even if we lifted the wrong guy he would think that you fingered him and so would the 'Ra' enforcers; if you think my colleague was a bit rough - you would think the 'Ra' enforcers were sadists. They had a thing called the water torture where they half drown you twice a minute for hours. After two days of that they would get you admitting to raping your granny."

Pearse Gormley felt morally outraged. How could they do such a thing to him. His fuddled mind could not cope with the enormity of being an outcast in his own community. He was a soldier in the Irish Republican Army and he was captured and he should be treated like a prisoner of war. Now they were talking about letting him go and branding him an informer. Perhaps if they let him go he could just go to England where his two brothers and sister lived and forget about the whole business.

"If you are thinking about going across the pond to your brothers forget it. We will put a restriction order on you so that you can't land in England and if you went over the border the enforcers would have you in a week."

Ramsey had used this ploy many times before and had followed his prisoners lines of thought.

Try as he would, Pearse Gormley could not disengage his mind from the problem that was posed by his interrogater. He knew he should say nothing but what if the let him go and lifted some of the boys whose names were mentioned. Some of them were bound to break over some of the operations in which they were implicated. He could not think straight. If only he could clear his head and think of a strategy that would not involve naming anyone. At this moment Sean Ramsey offered a way out.

"Look Pearse, here's what we will do. We won't make you sign anything. We will just charge you with the crime and release you from here to Crumlin Road Jail where you can go to the provo wing. Your barrister will plead not guilty. There is only the witness to say she saw you there and she might not be believed so you might get off without a stain on your character either with the law or with the 'Ra'. But you must give us the name of the driver."

"It was Sean McManus"

Pearse Gormley blurted it out without hesitation.

The phone call to Whiteabbey police station was made by McKillop.

"Pick-up Sean McManus at University of Ulster Irish Studies Department and bring him to Gough immediately."

Sergeant Ramsey drew a packet of Benson and Hedges from his pocket and lit two. He proffered one to Gormley.

"Thank fuck"

Gormley murmured as he drew deeply from the cigarette. Ramsey smiled then and Gormley smiled back symbiotically.

"It won't be that hard if you get sent down."

Ramsey said in a relaxed manner.

"The Provo wing in the Maze more or less runs itself. You can watch television all day if you want. There are lots of classes if you want to improve yourself. You could learn all about computers, they will even give you one. If you get fed up listening to all that holy Ireland crap you can tell the screws you want out and transfer to Maghaberry. Then it's only a matter of time before you get a review."

Ramsey talked on until seven o'clock when he called for a uniform man to escort Gormley back to the cells. McKillop punched Gormley in the kidneys as he left the room.

"That's for Gary Johnstone"

he said as Gormley doubled up in pain emitting a loud moan.

Sean McManus tried to make a break for it when the detectives cornered him in the lecture room in the University of Ulster on the outskirts of Belfast. The lecturer, who was a Sinn Fein supporter, immediately protested at the violation of the university campus. He was told that the campus had been already violated years before when a class of police students had been blown up by a bomb placed in the roof of their classroom. The lecturer then dismised his class and made a phone call to Connolly House, the Sinn Fein headquarters. The solicitor from Flannagan and Meehan was already at Gough Barracks when the arresting party arrived.

This time the suspect refused to say anything except that he didn't recognise his captor's authority. Sean McManus just stared at a spot on the wall and hour after hour repeated his mantra. The detective cajoled, threatened, entreated, insulted and provoked him but he just stared at the wall. It looked very like he was going to walk free when a break came.

Gary Johnstone's widow was deeply traumatised after the death of her husband. During the preparations for the funeral the police more or less took charge. The police band with muffled drums headed the cortege. The coffin was draped in the union flag topped by Gary's uniform hat and the chief constable walked beside the secretary of state and the army general. After the funeral was over Irene was sunk in a black depression and alone with her child. Her sister Jean and her mother moved into the bungalow to nurse her through her grief. One day when the mother was walking the dog near the bungalow the dog dragged a striped yellow and brown scarf from under the hedge. The mother knew that the police had searched the ditches for clues and knew the scarf might well be of significance. A hair fragment was found by the forensic laboratory which matched the DNA of a hair from Sean McManus's head. It was decided by the Superintendant to detain the two gunmen for the full seven days allowed by law to allow for corroborating verbal evidence before formal charges were made. Detective Sergeant Ramsey thought that perhaps Pearse Gormley would help with other information. Gormley however had regained his confidence and regretted implicating his accomplice. He steadfastly refused to submit to either blandishment or threat. Then a strange visit from an official from the Northern Ireland Office took place. The man was obviously a spook of some description but he had authorisation from the highest authority to do as he wished in the holding centre. He was tall, elegantly dressed in a houndstooth jacket and cavalry twills. His baby face sported a dark military moustache and a regimental tie completed the picture of a typical upper class Englishman complete with cut glass accent. He demanded to see Sean McManus in his cell before he was charged. The cells were on the first floor and the Englishman insisted on going up alone with the key. There was no noise at first but some moments later there were screams and thuds heard from the cell. McKillop and Ramsey exchanged glances before rushing out of the interview room to see McManus covered in blood, being hurled down the stairs. He had received a terrible beating and now lay at the foot of the stairs with a fractured arm.

"He's some pup,"

said McKillop as the NIO man donned his soft brown felt hat to depart the barracks as quickly as he arrived.

"I have been wanting to do that to the murdering bastard all week."

"I don't think that was at all necessary"

was the only comment that Ramsey made as he entered an accident incident in the day book. Sean McManus had fallen down the stairs for the record. An escort party was quickly gathered to take him to hospital where the casualty doctor encased his arm in plaster and dressed his wounds. He was then returned to the holding centre where he was formally charged with the murder of Constable Gary Johnstone.

On the day of the court hearing Sean McManus and Pearse Gormley were jointly charged with the murder. The court was heavily guarded, the atmosphere was tense as the barrister for the prosecution opened his case. He stated that both defendants were believed to be members of the IRA a pro-scribed organisation and there was a witness to their involvement, also foren-sic evidence. Jean Craig in a sober grey suit and white blouse, gave evidence of driving into the Johnstone driveway and seeing Pearse Gormley on the back of the motorbike and having a good view of his face when he turned around.

The barrister for the defence was a young alert but experienced advocate with connections in the Orange Order. He had charm and good looks and his fee cost the British taxpayer a thousand pounds a day.

"Miss Craig is it not true that you are a serving constable with the Royal Ulster Constabulary and a sister-in-law of the deceased"
he began.

Jean Craig lifted her beautiful brown eyes to regard the barrister and softly stated she was proud to be both.

The barrister shifted on his feet to position himself for the verbal assault that he was now set to deliver.

"Would it not be true to say that you were also his lover."

Irene Johnstone, still in mourning clothes, was in the well of the court. She gave a cry of anguish, then stumbled out of the court sobbing convulsively. Jean Craig's eyes were now blazing and here voice shook with anger, this being the desired effect of the barrister's provocation.

"That's a lie. Gary was my sister's husband and nothing else to me."

"Would it not be true to say that you had access to police files and you picked out some suspect on the grounds that any Taig would do. In other words someone had to go down for the murder of your brother-in-law preferably one with republican sympathies from the police files."

"That man there is the man I saw on the motorbike."

Jean Craig shouted this out and turned her blazing eyes away from the barris-ter in contempt. The barrister gave her a quick smile that said there were no hard feelings. It was only part of the game.

In fact the barrister was only playing games. He had a master card to play but he intended the trial to stretch out as long as possible while the meter was still running so to speak. Sitting in the corner of the public gallery was the tall man with the baby face and the military moustache. He was taking copious notes.

Irene Johnstone, her eyes red from tears returned from the corridor as the defence barrister made his plea.

"My lord, it has come to my attention that the accused Sean McManus and Pearse Gormley have been abused and in the case of Sean McManus badly beaten while in police custody. It is also my contention that both of them have been held in Police custody before being charged for longer than the seven days allowed by law."

The judge who lived in constant fear of his life because he was designated a legitimate target by the IRA, called the prosecuting and defence lawyers to his room. The senior policeman at the trial, was also called in the clarify the position. The policeman admitted that the seven day period was exceeded by the investigators but that the delay had been caused by the necessity of taking McManus to hospital after his fall. The defence barrister then produced a statement from the accident department doctor who treated McManus to the effect that the marks on his face could only be caused by a beating.

The judge of course threw out the case with caustic comments about the rule of law and the need for the police to obey the rules. In the corridor the tall baby faced man approached the chief superintendant and admitted that he had done what he had in order that Sean McManus would be an active player in the armed conspiracy.

"You see we know he has the ear of the top man and his ideas about the terror campaign are ambivalent. We think he is interested in a gradual political approach which will get them what they want. He is very junior still but in the fullness of time he will rise to the top and we will be able to do business with him."

No one noticed the uniformed Jean Craig moving to a position within earshot of the conversation.

"All scum rises to the top you know, even in the Northern Ireland Office."

This was her parting shot as she walked away to comfort her sobbing sister.

The Letter

The Letter

A grey hulled tramp steamer edged into the bay at the port of Colon in Panama. The deck was stacked with lumber from Canada, leaving only the funnel masts and rigging exposed and having only walkways clear for the sailors to get from the accommodation aft to the bridge. Rusty streaks ran down her sides, a dirty Liberian striped flag lay limp at her stern in the airless tropical fug. The ship's name *"Oceanus"* and the port of registry *"Monrovia"* had partially been washed away revealing the letters "EM" of empire and the letters "LI" of Liverpool underneath. This was an indicator of the ship's former British registry as the *"British Trust"* of Liverpool but the yellow, blue and black of the funnel placed the *"Oceanus"* firmly in the ambit of a well-known Greek millionaire shipowner. A shout in the Greek language from the bridge and the answering call "Malesta" from the bow announced the rumbling of the anchor chain as the anchor slipped into the muddy water of the bay. The telegraph on the bridge rang "stop engines" and, as the achor engaged, the ship slewed round to a position abeam of the tree fringed coast. As so often in the tropics the clouds spread apart allowing shafts of sunlight to illuminate the bay. Within minutes the bay was bathed in sunlight, steam rose from the jungle clad hills ashore and the white buildings of the port of Colon became visible to the sailors on the *"Oceanus"* for the first time.

Firemen and engineers emerged from the furnace heat of the engine room mopping their faces with sweatrags and breathing deeply of the first fresh air they had had in a four-hour watch. Sailors from their fore and aft stations made their way midships through the canyons of lumber on the deck to where the engineers and firemen had assembled just aft of the bridge and in front of the galley. Dressed in dirty jeans and sweatshirts and with their canvas caps and working gloves tucked in their hip pockets their rolling gait and demeanour distinguished them from the heat-exhausted firemen and engineers. The cook, an elderly man with a stained apron, thrust his head through the galley port hole.

"Eches Kaffee"

he announced as the second cook passed out steaming cups of black coffee to the lounging seamen. The Captain appeared on the aft side of the bridge outside the radio room overlooking the men lounging on the stacks of lumber. He was a middle aged small swarthy man, sway bellied and clad in clean jeans and shirt. He was in an expansive mood, pleased with his successful navigation of the American west coast and looking forward to the visits from the agents, with their customary deference to the Captain usually expressed with a small gift, but most of all to the letters from his wife. Normally he was a taciturn man who dined in solitary splendour and limited his conversation to the chief engineer, the first mate and the radio officer. Even at that, these conversations would be ranged around the running of the ship and he never confided his opinions to anyone. Today was different. He felt the need to banter with his ship mates, some of whom he had known for years on different ships and some of whom came from the same group of islands in the Aegean.

"Yasas patriotises"

he called out, signifying that although living in Cardiff for many years with his Welsh wife he still considered himself a patriotic Greek.

"Yassoo Kapetan Yorgi",

the men chorused politely and sensing that they were to be given a rare insight to Captain George's thoughts they ceased their conversation and gave their attention to their small but imposing Captain.

"What will you give the carpenter for making you a ladder from all this timber?"

said one swarthy middle-aged fireman who knew his Captain well from other ships and was also a villager from the same island. He knew well that the carpenter had been hard at work making a ladder and dog kennel and various other wooden articles since leaving Vancouver.

"I will give him a bottle of whiskey and my good wishes",

said the Captain. The fireman Ioannis also lived in Cardiff with a young Welsh girl whose ancestry was uncertain.

"Will you give me a bottle of whiskey for painting that mast?"

Ioannis responded.

"You wouldn't be able for it Ioannis. You would fall off it half-way up and then I would have to visit your woman in Cardiff and spend a lot of time consoling her while your bones would lie here in Panama",

laughed the Captain. Ioannis's brown eyes flashed at this and he bared his gold-capped teeth in a false smile. The smile was crooked due to scar tissue on his upper lip partially concealed by a pencil line moustache, the result of a knife fight with his brother-in-law in Piraeus ten years previously. He had not returned to Greece since. The second engineer, noting danger signals, challenged all comers to paint the engine room bulkhead for two bottles of whiskey provided he got them from the Captain and gave one to him, the second engineer. The banter continued and developed along the lines of the rivalry between the islanders and the Athenians. Ioannis, stung by the reference to his woman, lashed out with a ferocious Hellenic oath.

"Gamoten Panayia kai Nisia Epeesees! Fuck to the Virgin Mary and the islands too!"

he cried, mostly in self-hatred, as he shared with the Captain the island of Chios as his birthplace as did the millionaire who owned the ship.

"The pusti island shipowners live in luxury and fuck princesses off our sweat", he continued to the amusement of everyone.

"They steal our bread when they have nothing left to steal",

said the elderly cook who had now finished his chores and was lounging on the timber with a coffee and a cigarette.

"It is you who steals the bread",

said Captain George.

"From the amount of flour you use I think you must be posting it home to your family".

 "I make good bread",

said the cook.

"Look how fat Ioannis is and you too Kapetan Yorgi".

The banter between the Captain and crew continued until the third mate appeared on the bridge to annouce the approach of the agent's launch. A gleaming white motor launch pulled alongside as the sailors lowered a gangplank to receive the ships agent on board. He was an American in a spotless white linen suit who marched straight to the bridge in a business-like manner, leaving his black Panamanian boatman to make fast his vessel. Both the boatman and his vessel were immaculate, the boatman in a white matelot's uniform that accentuated his ebony skin and the boat's wooden deck scrubbed white and it's brasses gleaming. The boatman lit a cheroot and lazily waved a hand to the *"Oceanus's"* seamen all in the one movement. By this time they were lining the ship's rail anxious to observe, with the curiosity of those who have been deprived of outside human contact. The boatman then squatted on his heels, puffed on his cheroot and gently rocked back and forward. Above in the Captain's cabin the agent passed the ship's mail to the Captain and set about the business of completing the formalities for a passage through the canal. The boatman by now had finished his cheroot and was busying himself with sluicing down his white wood deck with buckets of seawater. He had removed his canvas shoes for this task, obviously enjoying the cool water running over his feet and between his toes. He mouthed a repetitive Afro-Caribbean tune in Spanish as he worked, lost in self-admiration and sensuality. The Greek sailors above shouted

"Bravo Hombre"

when he had finished and already the woodwork was steaming dry in the heat. Then without warning a gush of yellow liquid, soggy paper and indeterminate noisome matter poured on to the launch's immaculate deck. The water quickly flowed to the scuppers bearing with it the paper but leaving a homeric stool steaming at the proud boatman's feet. He stared at the offending object unbelievingly at first, and then, obviously outraged, he lifted the boat hook and swung at it like a demented golfer. He swung at it with such force that the turd stuck on the rusty surface of the Oceanus's hull. This seemed to give him some satisfaction as he looked up to the guffawing Greeks he smiled and shouted

"This is a sheet sheep."

The boatman fell to his sluicing task again unconcerned about his urine soaked feet and then lit another cheroot, squatted again on his heels, rocking rhythmically to the tune in his head.

The sailors at the ship's rail became bored so they interested themselves in the activities of the bosun who, armed with bucket and sharpened welding rod, was spearing the rainbow-coloured fish that weaved and ducked in shoals just below the surface of the water. The bosun hurled his spear at the water, causing the rope to which it was attached to uncoil so fast that the ship's cat scampered to the safety of the crew's accommodation. A writhing multicoloured fish not unlike a dogfish was hauled to the surface, the spear through its gills. The young English radio officer who had joined the spectators whooped with excitement.

"Quiet Marconi",

the bosun reproached,

The Letter

"You will skar the feesh".

He tapped the fish's head with a marline spike and withdrew the spear.

The colours of the fish seemed to change in contact with the air. It now seemed to be mostly grey and brown. The cat crawled across the deck and poked the now dead fish with her paw then seized it by the tail and made off with it before the bosun could stop her.

"Bravo gatos,"

cried one of the sailors,

"We will now watch the cat and if she is not sick we can eat the fish".

The bosun raised his face to the sun and laughed. Crows feet spread from his eyes, laughter lines creased his cheeks, his teeth spread white against his bronzed skin for all the world like Sitting Bull in early middle age.

"Son of a bitch cat!"

he said in English for the benefit of Marconi as he aimed his spear for another thrust. Soon the bosun's bucket was filled with dying fish and as the cat was still alive and apparently healthy, the cook started to gut the fish ready for the crew's tea. All the interest in the proceedings evaporated however when the chief mate arrived on deck with the mail. Ioannis the fireman had but one letter. It was addressed in big childish lettering and bore a British stamp. He opened it and pretended to read it but the writing meant nothing to him. After a sufficient perusal he made his way to the radio officer's cabin and politely knocked the door.

"Marconi, please no can read English. Greek can read very good. Speak English but no can read".

The young Englishman bade him enter, unfolded the letter and cast his eye over it. He knew at a glance from the first line that it was bad news so he asked the fireman to take a seat while he read.

Dear Yanni,

I know you will not like what I have to tell you but for nine months now I have been living with Domo who is a Maltese. I know you have been sending me the money every month but Domo finds it hard to get up in the morning and loses all the jobs. I needed the money to keep us as they stopped Domo's dole and we have to eat. Don't be angry Yanni as there was nothing else I could do. I know you will be home soon and I thought it was better to let you

know now. The weather is fine in Cardiff and I hope the weather is fine on the ship.
Love Yasmin.

Ionnis went white and clenched his fists. His eyes bulged and the young Englishman feared he would have a seizure.
"Take it easy old man. I will get the Captain to send a telegram and stop the allotment immediately. You are probably better off without her".
The scar on Ioanni's lip went livid and his eylid twitched.
"I will keel her",
he shouted.
"I will keel him as well, whoever he is".
The Captain appeared in the doorway alerted by the fireman's shouts.
"What is the matter Sparks?"
he said in English to the young radio officer.
"Ioannis here has had some bad news".
Ioannis turned an appealing face to the Captain and with palms outstretched he explained in a now quiet voice what had happened and what he would do when the ship arrived in Cardiff. The Captain listened and then raised his voice in anger.
"You will do no such thing. You will not sit in an English jail for that half caste whore. Putana innai! Tuxeres? She is a whore. You know that Ioannis? I will send a telegram to the owners and cancel the allotment. Here Sparks take this down. To Hadjipateras,Leadenhall Street, London. Cancel allotment Fireman Ioannis Koutsoukos to Miss Yasmin Roberts, Duke Street, Cardiff: Master *Oceanus*".
The radio officer started the transmitter generator saying
"I had better raise Portishead now as I can't transmit inside the canal zone".
He fiddled with the receiver until he found the station he wanted and then rattled on the morse key for a reply. The reply came in a steady rhythmic morse.
"I am receiving you strength 5 old man, send your telegram on your working frequency".
Sparks retuned his transmitter, re-established contact, then deftly keyed off the telegram that would stop Yasmin's remittance.

The Letter

The pilot launch arrived with the pilot and a deck crew of West Indians who would take the ship through the locks. Cheerful big men of every hue from off white to black, they went straight to their stations fore and aft. The pilot, an American, gave the order to hoist anchor and start engines while the Captain translated his commands into Greek for the quartermaster. The Greek sailors and firemen still lounging aft of the wheelhouse were now eating the fish the bosun had caught and Ioannis the fireman, who had the best English, offered one of the West Indians share.

"Have some feesh. Very good for the brains".

The West Indian shook his head and produced a small aluminium tube which he proffered to Ioannis,

"Have some of this man. It is very good for the womans".

"What is it?"

Ioannis said.

"Chinese paint man. You put it on your dick and you can stand all night."

The other Greeks had caught enough of the conversation to become interested.

"Ti Innai afto? What is it Ioannis?"

"He wants to sell aphrodisiacs",

Ioannis told them.

"Only two dollars a tin man,"

the West Indian offered. The Greeks roared with laughter.

"You will need it when you get to Cardiff, Ioannis",

one of the firemen said. Ioannis swore a fearsome oath and shouted

"Te xerete gamoto yia tin yuneka mou? What do you know about my woman?" Ioannis had sworn Marconi to secrecy about the letter and Captain George had to respect his privacy as his Captain and his fellow islander. He rushed into the accommodation to hide his anger. As is the nature of things in a small community his secret had got out through the chief engineer who had been told by the Captain to watch Ioannis to make sure he didn't harm himself.

The ship, now underway, slipped into a convoy of other vessels making passage, past the jetties of Colon port and into the canal. Up on the bridge the pilot chatted with the Captain, telling him of other Greek crewed ships he had taken through recently, of who was master and chief mate and of where they were bound. The jungled hills of the isthmus slid by, colourful birds flew through the rigging until the first locks appeared. This involved the West Indians in much slackening and tightening of ropes as the electric mules hauled them up to the next level of locks. Those off watch could relax, admire the American women who gathered on the shore to watch the ships make passage. The Panamanians had seen it all before. Eventually the *Oceanus* tied up at the port of Cristobal on the Atlantic shore to load bunkers to see her across the Atlantic. Four hours of shore leave was allowed by the Captain. This information was passed on by word-of-mouth. The chief mate, known to the crew as Lefteros Kapetanos Stilios or Second Captain Stilios, a man of much experience and few words, talked to the young Englishman as they made their way along the palm fringed road that led to the town of Cristobal. Marconi asked the older man what he thought the fireman Ioannis would do when the ship reached Cardiff.

"I know him of old," said the mate.

"He will surely kill her. He is a violent man. He carries a knife since he was stabbed by his brother-in-law in a Piraeus taverna for going with putanas. He is a jealous man too and the Malteser would be better to go home for a holiday while we are there."

The Englishman opined that the fireman was well shot of her no matter what it cost him. At the approaches of the town they passed an Indian woman with a child.

"Donde esta la casa Greca?"

asked the mate who knew of a Greek night club in Cristobal. She indicated the second street at the right and soon they arrived at the door of

"El Paradiso Greco".

The swing doors lead to a room with a dance floor surrounded by tables. Only the circular dance floor was illuminated by a spotlight, the tables being in semi-darkness as were the three bored musicians who were lolling on their seats puffing on cheroots. A few bull-necked American contruction workers sat at tables with skinny under-age Indian girls. Two white pillars framed the band and indicated that the club had once been a warehouse. The only thing Greek about this particular paradise was the owner who, recognising a fellow countryman, greeted the chief mate in effusive Greek.

"Kalos eerthate lefteros Kapetanos."

"Marconi here is English, we will speak English",

said the mate.

"Thank you Kapetan Stilios", said the Englishman.

"I see the fireman Ioannis and Nicos the bosun over there. We will join them."

"Certainly gentlemen, I will bring you ouzo on the house".

Ioannis and Nicos the bosun were shaved, perfumed and decked out in white shirts and clean jeans. Nicos's good humoured face contrasted with the sullen demeanour of the fireman. They both stood up out of respect for the ship's officers but lapsed into easy conversation in Greek. Now and then they would translate a point that they thought might interest the Englishman but mostly they spoke of the running and maintenance of the ship as sailors will when they are ashore. The patron joined them with a tray of ouzo glasses.

"Eseegea Patriotis",

said the patron as the company raised their glasses. Ioannis downed his drink in one gulp and called for more ouzo and beer as well. The patron signalled to a waiter as the musicians hefted their instruments for the cabaret. Three sad looking and tired mulatto girls appeared in the spotlight and bowed to the Greeks's table. Nico the bosun rose and returned the gesture but Ioannis only glared and muttered

"Putanas"

under his breath. The mulatto girls gyrated with more action than feeling and finished their act by wrapping themselves round the white pillars simulating the act of love. Within minutes after their act they were dressed and sitting at the Greek's table. The waiter appeared immediately with ouzo and glasses of indeterminate liquid which he called

"Cocktails for the ladies".

The band played, the beefy American construction workers danced with their little Indian girls and the conversation at the Greek table got boisterous and loud. The three cabaret girls sat on the knees of Kapetan Stilios the bosun and Marconi, as they sipped their coloured water. Ioannis the fireman sat morose and uninterested in the stream of bad English jokes and sexual innuendo that passed for conversation. The table was piled with dirty glasses, overflowing ashtrays and spilled beer by the time Kapetan Stilios called for the bill.

"One hundred dollars altogether",

announced the waiter, the Greek patron now nowhere to be seen. This was at a time when one hundred dollars was more than a month's wages for a

seaman working seven days a week. The dancers slid quietly from the knees of the seamen, excused themselves with a
"Going toilet plees",
never to be seen again. Ioannis was the first to react. His scar went livid, his eyes flashed and his gold-capped teeth were bared like a dog's. He upended the table with a crash, sending broken glass and ashtrays across the floor. Then he took a swing at the waiter, missing but throwing himself off balance. Nicos the bosun lifted him to his feet, but he struggled free and lurched in the direction of the waiter, swearing fluently and ferociously the while. Marconi and Kapetan Stilios grabbed him by the arms and marched him towards the door. Kapetan Stilios left two fifty dollar bills on the cashier's table as they left, passing the Panamanian police on their way in.

The *Oceanus* sailed out of Cristobal scything through the calm blue Carribean with all the crew re-adjusted to the ship's routine of watches or daywork. The episode in the Cristobal night club was talked about for some days and then forgotten. Kapetan Stilios's generosity in paying the bill was however not forgotten, the bosun Nicos directing that his cabin be painted out while he was on watch. Ioannis the fireman, however, went about his work mechanically as he had done for twenty-five years, oiling moving parts, adjusting the fire jets, all with the air of a man with an unquiet mind. He spoke only to the second engineer when he had orders to take regarding the maintenance of the engines. As the ship battered through the grey North Atlantic rollers the Captain shared his worry about Ioannis's threat to kill his former lover.

"He is still a very angry man, Sparks. It is a very great insult to make a cuckold out of a Greek man, never mind the money involved. I think I will send a telegram to my wife in Cardiff to tell her to warn the girl".

The telegram was duly sent as the ship neared Cardiff roads. Tension on the ship was palpable.

The ship entered the Bristol Channel and steamed through a murky November night to lie off Cardiff roads waiting for the pilot who came on board at morning light. The agent was waiting with the stevedore on the dock and passed the mail to the Captain. There was no letter for Ioannis.

Ioannis, unshaven and in working clothes, sipped his coffee in the sailor's mess that morning, speaking to no one. The third engineer who also lived in Cardiff called into the mess, resplendent in dark blue suit and fedora hat, and was about to offer the fireman a lift in the taxi he awaited, but hesitated and then thought better of it.

Two days passed without Ioannis going ashore and the Captain confided in Marconi that the girl Yasmin had just shrugged her shoulders when warned of her former lover's smouldering mood.

"He will do what he will do",

was all she said.

Finally, Marconi the Englishman, the foreigner, who was stranger to the Greek ethos, approached the fireman on his own and asked about the situation.

"Marconi my friend, I will not touch her, I will not see her, my anchor has dragged, there is no berth here any more. Maybe I will go back to Greece, to my island away from Piraeus, if I can save enough money to buy a house. If not a ship will be my home. There is alway a job on Greek ship for Ioannis. I am very good with the fires in the engine room. Yes, I will not be the first sea gipsy nor will I be the last".

Dog Day

It's dawn already but they are not up yet so I will go back to sleep. I dreamed I chased the ginger cat last night but when I caught him I woke up. I was glad of that because I wouldn't like to hurt him really. Again he might hurt me with his claws so its best I don't catch him. I hear a noise in the bathroom. That's good because I feel lonely and I want to make sure they are still here. I hear footsteps on the stairs and now the door opens and it's her. Yes they are still here and I am glad so I jump up to lick her face and she give me a big hug. I don't really like that, I would prefer that she lick me like a dog but it seems to make her happy.

She lets me out into the yard where I usually smell around to see if any other creature has been there since last night. Sometimes I can smell the ginger cat and that really upsets me. I don't go into his yard. I don't even know where it is. He sometimes walks across the yard wall just to vex me. He knows I can't jump up that far so he doesn't even run away. He just stands there and arches his back, staring at me as if I was a creature from outer space. When he does that I howl and run round in circles although I know this doesn't achieve anything, but I do it anyway.

Then she will open the backyard door and I can get into the entry. The entry is a wonderful place full of the smells of all sorts of creatures. I can spend half an hour sniffing around it in peace. Then of course Max, the neighbour's dog will come out. I like Max, he looks like me with black and white shaggy hair and a beard. He did things to me once and later I had pups. I loved those pups and wouldn't let anyone come near them for a long time. I even growled at both him and her although I know they wouldn't harm them. It was a good time then, lots of people came to see them and made cooing noises over them. I was really quite proud and not at all jealous. I am jealous however about that Jasper retriever who comes round and thinks he owns the place. He seems to have been coming here before my time so I can't object but when he eats from my bowl it really is a bit much. I suppose it is custom and practice really.

When I get back in the house I want to go up to the bedroom and wake the master up. He stays in bed a lot longer than she does. I think he is ill or something. Sometimes I can jump on top of him and lick his face and then he shouts at her. Something about a damned dog. However if he is awake he is quite pleased to see me and ruffles my ears.

I would lie on the bottom of the bed until he gets up and when he come back from the bathroom he usually plays with me for a while. If he doesn't I will take his sock in my mouth and then he has to play with me to get it back.

My bed is in the dining room beside the fire and I will lie in it while he has his breakfast. My own food will be in my bowl but often I am not hungry and I just leave it there. If I can smell something sweet that he's having for breakfast I will put my front paws on his knee and whine until he give me a share. Sometimes he says,

"Eat your own grub"

and doesn't give me a share and if I keep whining he will either give me some or shout at me. I can understand a lot of things humans say if they talk to me directly. If they say

"There's the pussy cat"

I go berserk and run round in circles howling until they let me out. Sometimes they say it when there is no cat there but I am never sure whether the cat has gone or whether the cat was never there.

It takes a dog to be clever to get what it wants. The master says to her often that God made jellyfish smarter than me but I always know when he is going out. You see he always turns the radio off and the fire out. When I see him do that I will stand beside the door and sneak out in front of him. Then he either has to take me with him or go back to open the door to put me inside again. Very often he will just let me go with him in the car. I love the car. You can sit there and see everything that is going on. If I see a cat I howl and if I see another dog I will just growl. When he parks the car I just curl up and sleep if there is nothing happening. I always know he will come back although when she takes me to the place where there are a lot of cars parked and a lot of people going into the gloomy building with the steeple she is a long time coming out.

I love it when they take me to the house beside the sea. There is a big garden there with lots of fields to run about in. Not that I ever go far away. There is a big field at the back of the house with a lot of small trees and long grass. I would be frightened to go in there on my own because you never know what would jump out on you. You can smell the scent of a lot of strange creatures there like frogs and foxes and all sorts of creepie crawlies. You know what they smell like but you don't know what they look like. They could be the size of a donkey for all I know. I smelled a mouse once and I jumped back as I could hear it moving the grass. I was frightened but when I saw it I pounced on it as it was very small. It was quicker than me and it got away.

The master has a round soccer ball which he kicks for me on the garden. I run after it as fast as I can and catch it in my mouth and shake it. I try to burst it but it is too tough. If it bounces I can jump up and hit it with my head. sometimes I can hit it two or three times and this makes the people laugh. I love playing with that ball and if they forget to play with me I can carry the ball in my mouth and drop it at the master's feet to remind him. I really love chasing that ball. I get so excited that I run round in circles. I don't know why I do that but I do it anyway.

Then there is the beach. I can run there as far as I like and there are lots of different smells among the rocks. They are sea creatures I suppose and I have no idea what they look like but it is very interesting to smell them. I love to roll in the rotting seaweed. It has a very strong smell and as I said, I love strong smells although I get shouted at and then they bath me which I don't like.

Then there is the sea. I love to run in the sea and will even swim in it although I feel safer with four legs on the sand. I will swim out to fetch a stick even on a cold day.

Another thing I like to do is to go with him to the shop for the papers. There are all sorts of people on the road at that time and I love people more than anything. Sometimes I see someone I think I recognise and I jump up on them to greet them. They do not always like this, but some do and they talk to me. Then there are the pigeons. They are cheeky birds that walk on the pavement. If I see one I make a dash at it. You should see the flurry of wings and feathers they make. I never catch one because of the lead on my neck but frightening pigeons is a most enjoyable pastime.

At night she comes home and that is an occasion for great excitement. I jump on her and she hugs me and I lick her face. That is because you never know when a human goes away whether or not they will come back and I am very frightened of being alone. I don't like other dogs you see, having been with humans all my life I became dependent on them. It is not just because they feed you, you become one of their pack so to speak. The most terrible thing in life is to be left alone. It isn't natural.

At night they both watch the flickering lamp in the corner which bores me. I recognise the tunes it plays at different times. Then I will fetch the tawse which is the length of play rope they got for me. I will bring it to him and growl and he will try and take if off me. If he succeeds, which he doesn't always, he throws it at the clothes drying frame. If it falls to the floor that's OK but if it hangs on the rail I would be frightened. You see it moves when I touch it and I am frightened when things move that don't normally move. This makes them laugh though she often says
"Shush"
when her favourite soap is on.
Then they put off the light and go to bed. I always want to go with them but they always put me downstairs if I manage to get up there.
I sleep on the rocking chair with the old fleece on it but I am always glad when I hear noises in the bathroom in the morning.
It's not a bad old life really.

The Box

Pier 24 in New York harbour was still for the day. It was Sunday in August 1956. The heat was stifling. The German freighter tied up alongside Pier 24 appeared to be deserted. Most of the crew were either sleeping or had gone ashore to Eighty-Sixth Street where they could relax over a few beers and listen to German music. A pickup truck drew up alongside the gangway. A polythene cover was drawn over it's back. The driver left the vehicle to look warily to either side, then ran up the steps of the gangway. He found the Captain's stateroom and knocked on the door.

"I am the representative of Manhattan Export. I have the freight you were expecting."

The man spoke with an Irish accent.

The elderly white-haired captain asked if he needed some sailors to carry it on board. He hoped not as it was Sunday and he would be obliged to pay them overtime. The Irishman told him that the two of them could carry it up the gangplank and that the fewer people that saw it the better. A significant number of dollars changed hands and then the two men went down to the pickup. Under the polythene cover was a canvas covered wooden case. It had the name of a firm in Birmingham, England stencilled on the canvas. The two men carried the five-foot long box up into the midships accommodation where it was stowed away in the ship's sick bay. The Irishman gave the captain an envelope containing numbers of a latitude and longitude position and a password.

Eight days later the ship hove to at three miles off the coast of Donegal in the west of Ireland. The sea was middling rough but the captain could see a half decker of about eighteen foot bouncing over the waves towards the freighter. Aboard the half decker were three men one of whom wore oilskins. He was a lanky dark visaged man with a grey stubble and weather-beaten lined skin. The boat was plunging through the four foot waves, white foam sometimes breaking over the deck. The lanky man in oilskins steered it expertly adjusting the wheel to compensate for the force of the sea breaking over the port side. The other two men sat at the stern. They were young and bearded and both were dressed in blue jeans and ex-American army combat jackets dating from the Second World War. They were both obviously unused to the sea as they were ashen grey in colour. One of them who had a violent turn in his left eye leant over the side and vomited copiously. When he straightened up he swore furiously in a broad Dublin accent.

"This is a fucken bath tub with an engine. Why couldn't Paddy have hired a proper sea going trawler?"

The other man in oilskins spoke in a Donegal accent.

"Because there was no trawler skipper in Killybegs stupid enough to have anything to do with Paddy Gillespie. This bath tub as you called it has gone to Tory Island and back in a force eleven and if you get sick in a small lumpy sea like today you should stay away from the water."

The man at the wheel did not like his passengers. The other youth at the the stern had large even teeth and a badly pitted skin which showed even under his course black beard. He had cold brown eyes which narrowed when he heard the skipper's riposte. He was as sick as the Dubliner but was determined not to give way to his heaving stomach. In half and hour they reached the side of the German freighter. The off-watch sailors and firemen had started to fish for codling and mackerel over the side and responded to the Captain's request to carry the box out of the sickbay and lower it into the half decker by slip robe. The skipper of the half decker shouted up that he wanted a bottle of whiskey and a carton of cigarettes. The captain cursed.

"Ach du Scheisze! I vant away from here as soon as possible,"

Never the less he went back to his cabin and came back with a plastic bag which he tied to the rope which he lowered again.

"Greedy bastard, he'll get us all caught,"

said Blackbeard.

The box, which was about three foot broad and two feet deep, stabilised the half decker to a certain extent but the canvas cover had been torn in the transfer. Now, a heavy grey painted wooden crate was revealed with stencilled markings 'US Army G.T. Missile Mark 4' plainly visible. The skipper of the half decker eyed the box with a thoughtful look

"That ould box would come in very handy for a lobster keep boys,"

he said.

"I would paint over the markings and with the holes drilled in it for the sea to get in no one would be a bit wiser."

The Belfast man exploded with anger.

"Is there nothing safe from you? You greedy ould bastard. I'll plug you if I hear anything more from you."

"Ah give him the ould box for Christ's sake. It'll be less weight to carry." The Dubliner said this while lifting his head from the rail of the boat. There was silence as all three waited for a concensus to evolve. The boat was now close to the harbour and the engine was throttled back. Colour was coming back to the two landsmen faces.

"We'll give you the box provided you paint it over straight away and if you don't I'll come looking for you. Here's your twenty pounds and not a word to anyone."

The Belfast man handed the skipper the money as they rounded the pier end. The pier was crowded with trawlers. Rattling winches and the crash of fish boxes against the concrete made a cacophony mingled with the sound of fish lorry engines and the groaning and hissing of hydraulics. The boatman said to the two men as he tied up the half decker that they should pick up the cargo after dark and that they could take it out of it's case then. The two men nodded agreement, then made their way off the quays and through the back streets of the town. They stopped and entered a newsagent's shop set in a row of terraced houses with the legend 'Mac Giolla Espie' over the door in Gaelic script. The shop counter carried an array of local and British papers as well as Irish language publications. Behind the counter on the wall was a framed print of Patrick Pearse the leader of the nationalist insurrectionists in 1916. The shopowner was elderly and nondescript. He sported the badges of both Gaelic language speakers and total abstainers. His suit was greasy and his collar was frayed. He surveyed the two men with some distaste.

"Why don't you stick a label on your chest with IRA on it? Have you no other clothes than those Yankee army duds? Both of you with beards as well. In my day volunteers had to be clean shaven and wear a suit with a proper collar and tie. Anyway did you get the merchandise landed?"

They explained that the box was still on the half decker and that they were to collect it after dark.

"And you paid Hudie O'Donnell without getting the gear ashore! He'll be in the pub now and he won't be out of it till the money is spent. What sort of amadans are you anyway?"

The Belfast man was angry but he bit his lip to stifle the invective to which he wished to give tongue. The pair went through the back door to the newsagent's living quarters. They ascended the stairway to the room he had assigned them. The Dublin man opened his canvas rucksack to unravel a canvas wallet that contained a syringe and a capsule of clear liquid.

"Dammit I need more insulin. Remind me to get it in the morning before we leave."

He said this as he lowered his trousers to inject into a vein in this thigh.

"You are disgusting. Can you not do that in the toilet? You let us down too in that boat, puking over the side in front of the fisherman."

Blackbeard's nostrils flared as he said this. He seemed only a second from violence as he regarded his companion with distaste. The Dubliner, with his tully eye, appeared to be looking at the wall as his eyes blazed. Blackbeard accordingly failed to notice his reaction and presumed his strictures were ignored which made him more angry.

"I don't know why they sent me a fucken cripple to do an important job. You are a fucken imbecile! Do you know that?"

Tully eye lunged at him with the syringe catching Blackbeard in the arm. He shrieked with pain as the blood soaked his shirt sleeve. Fisticuffs followed until the newsagent appeared in the room forcing them apart with curses and blows. When the fracas had subsided and night had fallen, the three drove slowly down to the quay in the newsagent's old Morris van. They boarded the half decker and pulled back the tarpaulin that had covered the box to find a green five-foot rocker launcher and six rocket grenades lying in the well of the boat.

"Sufferin Jesus! The old bastard has taken the box and left the gear there for the world and his wife to discover."

The newsagent did not know that the other two had promised the fisherman the box and they did not enlighten him. The harbour was now still and only the gentle lapping of the sea against the trawler hulls accompanied their unloading of the cargo under the quayside orange light. The weapon was loaded and the three drove quickly out of the town towards Pettigo and the border. Some days later in Killybegs a Sergeant of Civic Guards, as the police in the Irish Republic are known, was patrolling the coast on foot past Hudie O'Donnell's house when he spotted the box with newly drilled holes in the lid among the scatter of lobster creels. He examined the box and spotted the US Army markings. There was no response to his knock on Hudie O'Donnell's door so he continued his patrol back by the headland to the town.

Guard Sergeant Lawless was a slow thoughtful man who bore with equanimity the ribbing his name and occupation attracted. He was a Dubliner who found the pressure of police work in the city overtaxing and had asked for a transfer to the remote northwest coast. He was a conscientious policeman none the less, who had rectified an apalling attitude to duty he found amongst the guards in the Killybegs barracks. Sergeant Lawless intended to draw his pension in twenty years time at the most advanced pay rate he could achieve. He had stopped the practice of guards taking sick leave and working on trawlers when they were short of crew, or digging turf on the mountain when they were supposed to be on patrol. For this he was not liked by many people who expected returns for past favours to guards. He was deep in thought about the box outside O'Donnell's house as he reached the outskirts of the town.

The 'Harbour Lights' was a fisherman's pub which was busy at most times of the day or night as it had a twenty-four hour licence due to the arrivals of thirsty trawler crews at all times. This lunchtime half a dozen fishermen off the *'Moncallo'* were drinking pints of stout with Hudie O'Donnell who was flushed with drink and boasting about a great catch of lobsters he had collected.

"Every creel had a monster by the tail,"

he boasted.

"Hoist your gear boys, here's trouble,"

said a grizzled weatherbeaten fisherman whose car was parked round the corner, as he noted the entry of Sergeant Lawless.

"I heard that,"

the sergeant said.

"Do you know I could do you for having the keys of your car outside and too much drink taken but couldn't touch you for having the key of the wheelhouse and you legless and going out to drown the whole crew."

Hudie O'Donnell straightened up on the appearance of the Sergeant but Lawless had already noticed the line of emply pint tumbers and whiskey glasses on the counter in front of him. He also noticed the packet of Lucky Strike cigarettes beside the empty tumblers.

"Had a good haul this morning Hudie?"

the sergeant nodded in the direction of the empties.

"The lobsters were lining up to get into the creels, Sergeant,"
Hudie replied with a hollow laugh.

The Sergeant had seen enough to satisfy his curiousity so he bade the fishermen farewell in a civil enough way and continued his patrol past Gillespie's newsagent's shop. He entered the shop to be greeted by a teenage girl who was a niece of Gillespie. He lifted a morning paper, perused it briefly and asked the girl about her uncle. The girl informed him that her uncle was away on business and would be back in a few days. Sergeant Lawless's mind was now centred on the three connecting facts that he had established. One, the box with the US Army markings, two, the new found affluence of Hudie O'Donnell and three, the absence from his place of work of the old republican Gillespie. He decided to go to O'Donnell's cottage after lunch when the drink might have loosened the fisherman's tongue. However, when he arrived at the cottage he received no reply to his knock so he entered the cabin living room. He found Hudie slumped fast asleep in the armchair. He wakened him roughly. The man blinked but before he had gathered his wits Lawless taxed him about the lobster keep in his yard.

"Sure it floated in with the tide Sergeant."

Hudie had his story ready as the visit of the Sergeant to the pub had unnerved him.

"I suppose the Yankee fags and the German brandy floated in on the tide as well?"

Lawless had noted the brandy bottle on the table.

"No, not at all Mr Lawless, I got that given to me by the cook on the Norwegian klondiker that was here last week."

Hudie had been skimming the edge of the law all his life which gave him the confidence which every liar needs. The Sergeant knew he was defeated but cautioned Hudie to report to the guards any knowledge he had of any subversive activities. He knew as he said it that Hudie would be signing his own death warrant if he did.

As he walked the road back to the barracks he pictured in his mind the map of Donegal. The nearest point to the Northern Ireland border was the tiny hamlet of Pettigo which was a village actually divided by the frontier. Then there was a direct road to the market town of Lifford which was also on the border but was unlikely to be the scene of and IRA attack. When Sergeant

Lawless reached the barracks he phoned the Guard station in Pettigo requesting the sergeant in charge to look for a red Morris van in the vicinity. The sergeant there ordered the other guard stationed there to go to the farm of a well known IRA sympathiser to question the farmer regarding the van. Pettigo is a curious place in that it once was the scene of an official Irish Army invasion of Northern Ireland. A column of the newly formed Irish Army occupied the village of Tullyhommon in 1922. However, the arrival of a British Army Royal Artillery battery convinced the Irish Army commandant that the border settlement would be upheld and the Irish retreated back to Pettigo. The hinterland of Pettigo is windswept moorland with isolated homesteads on the mountain side. It was common knowledge that the area was used from time to time as a weapons training camp by the IRA. The local sergeant and the investigating guard knew this but preferred to turn a blind eye to these activities due to the ambivalent attitude of the Irish government to the activities of such illegal organisations.

It was with this attitude that Guarda Sweeney approached the hill farm of Sean Doherty. Doherty's farm of heather and rocks swept for miles across the mountainside and into the valley below, which was hidden from the road. He was a batchelor in his fifties who eked out an existence on the dole plus profits from the flock of sheep that roamed his land. It was a sunny day with the shadows of the clouds scudding across the purple mountain. Guarda Sweeney sweated as he pushed his bicycle up the steep lane to the farmhouse. He would have been happier digging the cut of turf he had rented on the mountain on the other side of Pettigo and he was shrewd enough to know that the sergeant had sent him on this politically sensitive errand to avoid being involved himself. As Sweeny approached the whitewashed farmhouse he could see that there was no van in the yard. He knew of course there was a shed of sorts for keeping hay in the valley beyond the rise in the hill. This he knew to the the area the IRA used in the past for training and he had no intention to walk the extra mile to look at it. Sweeney knew he could be observed from the farmhouse for the past half hour but nevertherless gave warning of his approach by whistling loudly in the quiet summer air. Sean Doherty, recognising the guard's approach to his political allegiances, welcomed him to his house and offered him a cold bottle of stout. The inside of the house boasted a flagstone floor and a lime washed granite fireplace illuminated by a turf fire.

"Thank you Sean,"

the guard said in a semi-official tone.

"Would you have seen a red van hereabouts this last couple of days?"

"N'er a sign of one. Sure what would a van be doing up here on the mountain?"

Doherty gave the assurance that he knew was required and then lapsed into routine conversation about the weather and the crops.

The guard finished his stout, gave the customary request for further information and mounted his bicycle to freewheel back to Pettigo. Back in the station he reported his interview to the sergeant who entered an enquiry visit report into the station log book. A phone call to Sergeant Lawless in Killybegs emphasised that investigations had been made in all the likely quarters with a negative result. Lawless however could tell from his voice that only a perfunctory investigation had taken place causing him to go once again on his patrol past Hudie's cottage to consider his position. The smell of fish and seaweed always had a calming effect on Lawless. As a boy on the north side of Dublin he would go on his own to the fishing harbour of Howth where the sound of the seabirds, the rattle of the winches and the staccato trill of the fish auctioneer fascinated him. He had even persuaded one of the skippers to take him on a trip which proved to be a disaster. He had been so seasick that he really thought he was going to die. That ended his love affair with the sea but he still loved the ambience of a fishing port. Lawless's father had been a sergeant in the old Dublin Metropolitan Police who had imbued him with the principle that the rule of law separated civilised man from the barbarian. A lonely child, the after-thought of a large family that had scattered to all parts of the globe, he set about preparing for the Civic Guard examination which he easily passed. He accepted the fact that the policeman by nature of his job is set apart from the rest of society. He resented the chicanery by which politicians achieved immunity from minor crime for themselves and their friends. He knew of rapid promotion for worthless policemen achieved by cultivation of politicians. He resented this greatly as he resented the pusillanimity of the guards in Pettigo. He walked past Hudie O'Donnell's cottage to observe an old sea stained lobster keep lying beside the rocket case. Hudie obviously had not hauled his pots for some days. No doubt he would find him in the 'Harbour Lights' when he finished his patrol.

The pub was packed when he reached it. Two of the herring boats had landed a big catch and Hudie who had not been to sea for some days was carousing with the best of them. Lawless made his mind up to follow up his search for the contents of the box.

That night Sergeant Lawless phoned a friend who worked in the Guarda headquarters in Dublin Castle. He phoned his friend to his home to avoid eavesdroppers. His request was simple. He wanted the name and address of the front shinner in Pettigo. The return phone call the next day was abrupt. The name was Sean Doherty and the address was Mullaghdreen, Pettigo. The following day he donned his civilian suit and trilby hat, left a message in the day room that he had gone to county headquarters in Letterkenny, then he set out in his Ford Prefect for Pettigo. The summer weather continued to be fine with a warm southwesterly ruffling the heather on Mullaghdreen mountain. Michael Lawless was forty-five but his hair was thin and white, his nose had grown boney with broken veins. He knew he looked like a policeman so he stopped short of the village of Pettigo. He loosened his tie, took off his jacket and leaned against the bonnet of the car to soak up the mild sunshine. Eventually a cycling postman appeared on the brow of the hill.

"Would that be Mullagdreen Mountain?"

Lawless said, pointing to the low mountain with the cabin just below the summit. The postman told him that he didn't know the name of the mountain but the townland was called Mullaghdreen which was the information Lawless wanted to know without asking. He told the postman that he was from the Ordinance Survey Department and indeed he had left two striped sticks in the back seat of the car to evidence his story. He could see that the lane up to the cabin was observable all the way so he decided that the best approach was directly across the bog towards the back of the house which had no rear window. When he had cleared the back of the house he reached to rough path that led to the summit. He could discern tyre marks in the dry dust which quickened his pulse. Once he had broached the summit he saw what he knew would be there beside the wooden shed and it was Gillespie's red van.

Commandant Brosnan was in charge of the company of Irish Army infantry that maintained Finner camp in South Donegal. Finner is a hutted camp built by the British and now used for training the FCA who are the part-time reserve for the Irish Army. Brosnan found that the reserve officers always wanted to do the training themselves so he found time heavy on his hands. He was an ambitious officer still in his thirties and he knew well that a man could be overlooked in this outpost of the Republic, so to speak. He tried to keep his men busy with guard duties, firing practice and the like but he knew his reports to battalion headquarters made dull reading. He also had a pride in the army and his rank in it and resented bitterly when he read the press releases of the IRA signed by so called OC's of the South Donegal brigade of the IRA. He knew these people to be a small gang of violence-addicted zealots from Bundoran and if he had his way he would put them in military custody.

When Commandant Brosnan got the phone call from Guarda Sergeant Lawless in Killybegs about ground-to-ground missiles being mounted on the border he was furious. How dare they usurp the Army's function in this manner, he thought. Then, his enthusiasm rising with the thought of a report of a successful military action, he promised to mobilise his company and meet Lawless on the road at the foot of Mullaghdreen mountain. Lawless knew that the involvement of the military would forestall any political interference from the Ministry of Justice where pro IRA sympathy was sentient. The Commandant had studied the terrain meticulously before committing his soldiers, who, blackened up and camouflaged, spead out along the blind side of the mountain. Sergeant Lawless, this time in uniform, to uphold the primacy of the police as the civil power, led the way with the Commandant and his troops warily advancing in the line behind him. Lawless had told him that there might be any number of IRA in the shed and expect fierce resistance. Brosnan was pleased to see his soldiers fan out the way they had been taught, crouching as they half ran through the rocks and heather, the occaional flash of sunlight on their fixed bayonets the only visual indication of their presence. He made a mental note to recommend the use of camouflage cream on bayonets to the Ministry.

Inside the shed another drama was unfolding. Blackbeard and Gillespie, the newsagent, were standing with their hands in the air, backs to the wall. The tully-eyed Dubliner was swaying on his haunches pointing a loaded revolver at the pair. The Dubliner's eyes were glassy and his speech was slurred. The other two were obviously terrified, listening to the garbled rantings of their erstwhile companion with the concentration of a mountaineer who knows that any mistake may mean instant death.

"Staff Captain Frank Maguire, captains courageous, captains and the kings, Captain Midnight, Captain Death, captain how are you, captain shite. Knife, fork, plate and spoon, Tim Finnegan's going home. Finnegan's wake, Micky Finnegan, Micky Mouse, cat and mouse, cheese for the mouse, nothing in the house, house of the rising son, Rising Sons of Erin, Erin go bragh."

The Dublinman's revolver hand was now swaying from side to side as he rocked back and forth on his haunches. His terrified prisoners were muttering prayers visibly when, to their immense relief, two soldiers appeared in the doorway with Lee-Enfield rifles raised to their shoulders. Their appearance distracted the tully-eyed Dubliner sufficiently for Blackbeard to dive on him with shouted curses and rained blows.

"You crazy Dublin bastard you might have killed us."

By this time the Dubliner had collapsed into a diabetic coma and was unaware of the blows raining down on his face. One of the soldiers who could not have been more than sixteen clubbed Blackbeard on the shoulder with his rifle as the other lifted the revolver from the floor. Soon Sergeant Lawless and the Commandant were through the door to make the formal arrest.

Gillespie by this time had recovered his composure sufficiently to distance himself from the other two.

"What the hell kept you? This crazy bastard highjacked me with the van and forgot to take his insulin and was going to shoot us."

"Did he highjack Hudie O'Donnell's boat as well then?"

Lawless knew that O'Donnell would tell everything to avoid a jail sentence so he acted as if he had his confession already in this notebook. Blackbeard, still rubbing his shoulder, drew himself up to his full height and facing the Commandant announced:

"As a volunteer in the Irish Republican Army I refuse to recognise the legality of the Free State armed forces. I refuse to make a statement."

The commandant examined the rocket launcher and wondered how an illegal organisation could afford to buy such weaponry while the official army of the state were issued with old Lee-Enfield rifles with ammunition strictly rationed.

At the Special Court in Dublin Hudie O'Donnell claimed he was coerced as did the old republican Gillespie. They were both found not guilty and resumed their lives in Killybegs, with O'Donnell, much to the disgust of Gillespie, claiming to be something of a republican hero. Blackbeard and tully-eye both refused to recognise the court and got six months imprisonment followed by internment until the border campaign fizzled out. Blackbeard became a scrap car dealer in Belfast and later was convicted of the murder of a Protestant milkman for which he served eleven years. The tully-eyed Dubliner foreswore violence, became a socialist and became active in the Labour Movement in Dublin. Sergeant Lawless was transferred to a remote village in County Mayo where he did his duty conscienciously while he waited for a change of government. Commandant Brosnan received promotion to colonel and a transfer to Western Command headquarters where he was put to writing infantry training manuals. It had been the first time the Irish Army had been in the newspapers that year.

As he was leaving the dock after his aquittal Hudie O'Donnell was heard to ask the Guard Superintendant

"Is there e're a chance of getting back the ould box?"

Captain Courage

Of course Reuben Shite was not his real name. His real name was Reuben
Foy. His unfortunate sobriquet was not meant personally, having to do with
his occupation as a trawler skipper sailing out of the County Down coast.
Reuben was very greedy and when the cod-end of the trawl was inched up
on deck Reuben would inspect its contents. If there was more than thirty
percent of sea-wrack, stones, dead shells and other detribus of the sea bed
amongst the fish he would denounce the haul to the world as a bag of shite.
Reuben Foy sat in the wheelhouse of the *"Star of Hope"*, his slippered feet
resting on the wheel as the eighty foot trawler slowly nosed her way through
the flat calm February sea. He wore carpet slippers as he did not see any
reason for a good skipper to venture outside the wheelhouse if the crew were
moderately competent. Reuben was a low set man in his fortieth year, small
and muscular with thinning fair hair and deep set light blue eyes. Reuben Foy,
a man of irascible temperament, was a very successful skipper who risked
life and limb and that of this crew in seas that would send most fishing
skippers scurrying for shore. He judged that there would be a good haul this
tow as the boat's engine was labouring to pull the trawl through the water. To
the starboard side the thin winter sunshine glistened on the quarry faces on
the Mourne Mountains while the rugged outline of Peel Castle of the Isle of
Man gave Reuben his land mark to the port side. On the Very High Frequency
receiver a Portavogie voice crackled out
"Oney twa stane for yin in tow".
The Portavogie man spoke in broad Scots to fustrate any eavesdroppers.
Born into a seafaring family in Killglass, Reuben had gone to the Merchant
Navy Sea School in England before joining a Cunarder on the North America
run where he passed his Able Bodied Seaman's ticket. While in the United
States he realised that with the prevalent exchange rate an American seafarer
earned four times the money of a British A.B. The only way a foreign seaman could work of a U.S. registered ship was via a "pierhead jump". That
was the expression used to describe joining a ship at the last minute when one
of the American crew failed to turn up. Reuben jumped ship in New York and
waited every day for a month in the Seamen's Mission until a call came for an
A.B. to join a United Fruit Company freighter that was sailing that night.

He stayed with that ship for four years by which time he had the purchase price of the *"Star of Hope"* saved.

In the village of Killglass he became known as a fearless fisherman who would put to sea in a force nine gale if he thought there would be fish to be had. Once during a force eight gale while dodging through the North Channel he was summoned to the fo'csle by one of the crew who had heard a gurgling sound emanating from below his bunk. Lifting his mattress he found water bubbling through a gap between the timbers. Reuben simply grabbed a handful of straw from the mattress and stuffed it in the crack and continued on his passage to Tory Island in the Atlantic.

Another occasion on a bright Spring day, while the *"Star of Hope"* was on passage from Maryport in Cumberland to Killglass, the forward gear seized and try as he could Reuben could not free it. To call for assistance from another trawler would make him unpopular as the towing boat would lose a day's fishing, so Reuben examined his options. He could drift about 'not under command' and await a tow at the end of the day, or he could dodge the few miles into Maryport using the astern gear which was free. Reuben, however took a third option by heading on to Killyglass where he could allow his crew time at home and did not have to pay harbour dues so he put the engine at full astern and headed across the Irish Sea with the waves washing up across the square cut stern. Passing vessels called up their resting crews to see the extraordinary sight of an eighty foot trawler crashing through the sea like a seagoing bulldozer. Reuben docked his vessel perfectly at the harbour of Killglass where he had the gear box disassembled and repaired in time for the next day's sailing.

The *"Star of Hope"* was now yawing about with the weight of the trawl so Reuben gave the order to haul the gear. One of the crew operated the winch while the other two stood by the fore and aft metal gallows which held the running gear for the wire warps that drew the net. The trawl doors broke the surface giving the signal for the winchman to slow down and halt the spinning rums of the winch while the doors were detached from the warps thus allowing the net to be hauled up right to the gallows. A lifting rope was then attached to the middle of the net and hoisted up above the deck via a derrick on the mast. Then the crew could see whether or not they had a pay-day. Alas the net was full of heavy kelp stalks, literally tons of gnarled roots and leaves and only the odd lonely haddock and whiting in among it. The winchman pulled the cod end cord releasing the tons of seaweed on to the deck to be shovelled back into the sea. Reuben strode up and down the wheelhouse swearing fluently, giving voice to his anger and frustration by saying over and over again,

"No cod, only a bag of shite."

The crewmen whose remuneration depended on the cash value of the catch tried to console him by making reference to the wind being in the wrong art and the tide being on the turn. Stanley Peden, a grizzled veteran of sixtyone made some adjustment to the ground rope on the trawl.

"She must be too far down to catch all that wrack, I'll rise her up a bit."

Stanley's age and experience allowed him to take liberties with the running of the boat and generally his efforts were rewarding.

The trawl was run out again as the *"Star of Hope"*, now rid of the dragging netful of kelp, shot forward at a speed of ten knots.

The results of the next haul however were no better. An air of despondency hung over the boat broken only by Stanley's relentless good cheer.

"I can smell a good fry on the pan from that boat over there",

he asserted, pointing to a trawler that was at least half a mile away. Hugh Quigley, the sixteen year old boy who had just joined the boat, stuck his nose in the air, sniffed deeply for some time and then averred,

"I can't smell anything."

Even Reuben laughed at the youth's embarrassment when he knew he had been tricked.

As they steamed homeward the crew played poker in the fo'csle while Stanley built up their morale by remarks such as "we never died a winter yet".

"Reuben Shite must think he's never going to die, the risks he takes winter and summer."

This was the contribution of Aaron Mulhinch, a normally taciturn member of the crew who had gone to school with Reuben and was, to a certain extent, resentful of his success.

The early Spring light was fading as they rounded the pierhead into Killglass harbour where a hundred other boats jostled for position at the market dock. Most were landing dozens of boxes of prawns scraped from the sea bottom with the additional round and flat fish that were caught in the wings of the net. Their crews would expect to have a share of two or three times the amount of the average manual worker's wage. They paid for it in the coin of their own courage plus sweat and fatigue unknown since the last century.

Reuben and his crew tied up along the berthing quay without waiting for the fish auction where the fishermen traditionally would socialise and compare prices. They headed for their cars without even the usual parcel of fish for friends.

At the auction there were remarks passed about Reuben's quick departure. It was known that Reuben always abandoned the prawn fishery at this time of the year to search for cod and it was also known that he often landed hundreds of boxes when there was no other cod at the auction and received a premium price. When this happened all the other skippers would re-rig their nets and follow him So far there was no sign of any big landing of cod. The next day the crew of the *"Star of Hope"* sailed well before dawn and searched unsuccessfully for cod. At the end of the day they had a few boxes of cod and haddock, strays that had wandered off the shoals, as well as a few monk fish and squid but not enough even to pay for the fuel. Reuben paced up and down the wheel house muttering to himself,

"The bastards have to be there somewhere".

Days went by without any big catch. Aaron Mulhinch became more critically vocal, complaining about no meat on the table for his children. He kept quiet about his bank account with five figures entered on the foot of Reuben's success in landing massive catches when the prices were at premium level. One day in a nor' easter force seven, when the *"Star of Hope"* was inching forward on a huge swell of water to round the harbour wall, a following freak wave lifted the vessel bodily and flung her against the quay. Reuben gave the engine maximum rev's to try and drive her through the wave but nature was more powerful, a sound of splintering wood against stone was the signal that told him he was in collision. Several planks were splintered, luckily above the water line but the boat was in no condition to go the sea. The crew were really glad for the break they would have as they were working long hours for no money and they relished the thought of the luxury of a long sleep in a warm bed on a winter's morning. Not Reuben however. He was off to a carpenter's house that night where he wrested the carpenter from his TV to machine the planks that were needed to effect the repair. By three in the morning Reuben and the carpenter had replaced the damaged planks, caulked them and painted them, leaving the boat ready for sea at six in the morning. Still more days went by without any sign of the shoals of cod Reuben sought. One night they rounded the harbour wall of Killglass on a very high tide. Stanley Peden sniffed the air like a pointer and said,

"There's a sou' west gale coming up and its a full tide and as sure as there's shit on the tail of your shirt there'll be a good fishing at the F and F for a good few days."

The F and F meant the co-ordinates on the Decca navigator which showed the position of the boat at sea. That night on the BBC shipping forecast the announcer gravely warned of storm force ten in the Irish Sea. At six the next morning the crew gathered on the quary beside the *"Star of Hope"* expecting to be told that there would be no sailing that day. The sky was black, the sea was black and the land was black. There seemed to be a threatening hum in the air although as yet the sea was flat calm.

Reuben announced that they were steaming for the F and F half way to the coast of Wales. The crew let go the ropes and the roar of the Gardner engine shattered the calm of the harbour. Reuben ordered everything to be made fast or stowed away. Years of experience told Stanley and Aaron to tie up the cupboards, the oven in the cooker, the calor gas bottle and everything else that was lying about loose. The eerie low pressure hum in the air gave way to a high pitched whine signalling the imminent presence of high winds. An hour's steaming south and the boat's bow began to dip into the ten foot waves. In another half hour's steaming the wind was shrieking through the rigging at thirty knots. The waves were now twenty foot high forcing Reuben to throttle back the engine to six knots. The boat's bow was now dipping ten feet into the waves. The stores in the fo'csle were noisily crashing about in their cupboards. Hugh, the youngest sailor, felt his stomach turn over; Stanley and Aaron had thoughtfully lined their stomachs with dry brown bread. Up in the wheelhouse Reuben's blue eyes squinted under his Canadian fur hat as he scanned the wave tops ready to turn the bow into an abnormally high wave coming from the quarter. Every other minute he transferred the Decca reading to the chart. They still had another hours steaming to reach the point where the red F line met the purple F line. It was now eight o'clock and near dawn and the wind was howling at seventy knots. The ship's bow was now pitching into the thirty foot waves sloughing off three tons of water when she rose.

"She'll not rise if two waves come on her quick",

Aaron said, ever the prophet of doom. Stanley was jockeying to keep his balance as he struggled with the kettle to make tea.

"Here, take that up to the Skipper and quit your whingeing",

Stanley replied as he busied himself with bread and cheese. Hugh was comatose on his bunk, rolling from side to side with the pitching of the boat. In the wheelhouse Reuben was steering with one hand and holding the VHF microphone with the other.

"Rose of Sharon! Rose of Sharon! Rose of Sharon! Star of Hope! Star of Hope! Star of Hope! Can you hear me? Over."

There was no reply as every coaster and trawler on the Irish Sea had headed for port and by now was secured fore and aft and with quarter ropes against the storm.

At last they reached the co-ordinates. Reuben put the engines out of gear and engaged the power take off for the winch. Clad in his oilskins Stanley edged forward to the winch. Clutching at anything solid to avoid being pitched into the sea by the now violently yawing boat. Somehow Hugh managed to struggle into his oilskins and get himself on deck where, with Aaron, he grabbed the cod end and heaved it overboard. Reuben engaged the engine ready to surge forward but the propellor had lifted out of the water with the yawing of the boat and a deafening roar answered his pressure on the throttle. Without the restraint of the water the propeller spun at a terrifying rate, sending a paroxysm through the *"Star of Hope"* which opened a seam in one of her bulkheads. The boat's stern settled and she shot forward, the two sailors playing out the net as fast as they could. Then the winchman opened the clutch and the wires sped out through the rollers. Holding on to the gallows for dear life, Aaron and Hugh buckled on the trawl doors as the side-on waves crashed down on them. As the trawl doors opened against the sea, the boat regained some stability so Reuben cautiously inched up the throttle until they were making four knots. The towing of the long trawl against the water acted a a drogue and although huge waves were breaking over the deck the *"Star of Hope"* was no longer rolling so much.

The crew lay down on their bunks exhausted with the effort of just staying upright on the heaving pitching vessel. Reuben scanned the echosounder for the black thumb print like mark that identified shoaling cod. Stanley was right. Within minutes the thumb prints came up on the sounder paper, one, two, three; one after another. They were in amongst them. The black clounds skudded across the sky bringing sheets of freezing rain that served to flatten the white tops of the thirty foot waves. Stanley, the complete sailor, opened the engine room hatch in the cabin floor to find the engine room in six inches of water. He started the bilge pumps immediately. He waited with baited breath until the water level began to ebb. The pumps could cope if the leak didn't get any worse. He decided not to tell the others as Hugh was now very frightened as the effort of working had ceased and his mind was dwelling on the danger. The waves were still crashing on the bow, sometimes not being drained by the scuppers before the next wave crashed down. There was a real danger of the vessel being swamped by the weight of water. Hugh was now praying out loud. Up in the wheelhouse Reuben stood with legs akimbo, straining to keep his balance while he followed a well plotted course to capture the shoaling cod. They would have to hold on by their eyebrows when the net was hauled, he mused.

Four hours later he summoned the crew on to the deck. Stanley slipped and slithered to the winch while the other two hugged the steel gallows with all their strength. The winch was slipped into gear and the drums began to turn slowly. A sideways wave broke over the starboard gallows Hugh with it along the deck. The wooden toggle in the neck of his oilskin jacket caught in the moving wire warp, dragging him to certain death in the winchdrum had Stanley not stopped it in time. Reuben shouted from the wheelhouse.

"Get on your feet Hugh. You are too young to die. Lash yourself to the gallows if you can't hold on".

Hugh edged along the ship's rail to the gallows and gave himself two turns round the body with a mooring rope, fastening the other end to the upright of the gallows. The hauling of the net continued slowly. The weight on the winch was such that sometimes the clutch slipped giving rise to fears that they had picked up a bagful of rocks. Eventually the trawl doors broke surface and were safely slipped and lashed to the gallows. Then the net broke the surface like a silver mound in the black heaving sea. It was full of fish.

Reuben was now excited. Stanley cautiously crawled on his knees to the ship's rail and as the ship rolled to the starboard side he clipped on the hauling rope to the belly of the net. He lapped it twice round the hauling drum and slowly raised the bulging silver bag above the deck. It swung dangerously over the deck so he quickly let it fall in an avalanche of huge silver fish. Reuben swore from the wheelhouse as the many hundreds of huge codfish slithered about the heaving deck. Several stone of fish went over the side as the retreating weight of water cleared the ship's rail.

"Open the fish hold! Never mind the boxes or the pound. Get the fish below deck before we lose it all",

shouted Reuben. This was a dangerous manoeuvre as the breaking waves could flood the fish hold. There was a mountain of cod on the deck and it would have to be shovelled into the hold between the breaking waves. Stanley and Aaron loosened the chocks that secured the bar holding the tarpaulin that covered the planks of the hatch. They removed one of the hatch planks which was immediately carried to the scuppers by the retreating wash. Hugh struggled up with three shovels. All three shovelled furiously, pushing the mountain of cod through the gap in the hatch. Sometimes a freak wave would carry the cod with it through the gap seriously threatening the stability of the ship. Twenty frantic minutes saw the load of cod safely below decks, the hatch again made fast and the crew lying exhausted on their bunks. The net had again been shot. With adept seamanship Reuben had turned the bow round to trawl back up the course he had come. Reuben threw his fur hat in the air and danced a jig in the wheelhouse. The sea was now at their stern carrying the boat with it in great forward surges.

The next haul was equally productive the the *"Star of Hope"* was now well down in the water and the crew bruised and exhausted. Reuben was prevailed on not to make another tow. Hugh managed to stay on his feet long enough to make a brew of tea and some corned beef sandwiches. Reuben was calculating how much the catch would fetch when they got it to the market. They rounded the harbour wall and for the first time in twelve hours they were able to relax their muscles but their travails were not over. First the cod had to be winched out of the hold and gutted, boxed and cleaned, then winched on to the quay for the market. This was another three hours work which was carried out in the silence of exhaustion. Uncharacteristictly Reuben joined in the work but it was after midnight before the cleaned and boxed cod were on the quay.

The wind was still howling round the chimneys of Reuben's bungalow as he sank into the arms of Morpheus between satin sheets as his wife looked down on his sleeping form. His wife, to whom he refered unromantically as 'a sturdy wee woman', saw the deeply lined face, the thinnning fair hair and the sunken eyes with tenderness and pity. She had a house of stylish ostentation, all the modern conveniences she desired and the most expensive clothes out of the catalogue. Yet she knew in her heart that these were mere baubles to signal Reuben's success at the fishing. When she saw him he was invariably staggering from exhaustion and she often wished he would take a job ashore with time to enjoy some shared life together. She knew this was impossible, he would always be married to the *"Star of Hope"*. There were one hundred and fifty boxes of prime cod landed. The first buyer on the quay bid £5,000 for the lot.

Reuben accepted even though he thought he could get more for them when the other buyers arrived. There had been no other fish landed in the port that day due to the storm but Reuben knew when the word got round the other skippers would follow him out to the F and F to share in the spoils.

The crew were still hollow eyed and weak from exhaustion when they let go the ropes at six in the morning. The boy Hugh was dreading the trip but Stanley kept reminding him of the share he would collect on Saturday morning.

"It will be at least a grand if we get another few tows like yesterday"
he assured the boy. This thought lifted the boy's spirits and he found that half and hour out to sea he had regained his strength. The wind had fallen away to force six so there was no water breaking over the deck and it was safe to move about. Several twinkling lights to the stern told Reuben that some of the skippers had re-jigged their nets and were following him. He was half an hour ahead of them and he reckoned that the shoal had moved southeast of the F and F. Records of tows in previous years helped him determine the spot to shoot his gear.

The first tow filled fifty boxes which was easily gutted and stowed away. The second tow at daybreak showed four trawlers in a line beside him. Some of them had more powerful engines than the *"Star of Hope"* but he managed to inch ahead of them and the haul amounted to a respectable thirty boxes.

That night Reuben received £4,000 for his catch. After landing the catch Reuben headed straight out again and fished round the clock until the end of the week. By this time vessels from Fleetwood, the Isle of Man and Howth were crowding the area but Reuben had filled his fish hold five days at premium prices. The boy Hugh rushed home to his mother with £1,100 in cash on Saturday and was rightly proud of himself.

This, the story of the winter cod season, was repeated every year with Reuben Shite cursing when the cod weren't there and dancing when they were.

On a bright June morning some years later, Reuben, Stanley, Aaron and the now seasoned fisherman Hugh, stood in seaboots and jeans on a long plank suspended by two ropes from the rail of the *"Star of Hope"*. They were 'painting up' the hull which was badly scraped by the friction from the metal trawl doors. They stood, stripped to the waist in the warming sunlight, all in good humour with badinage flying back and forth.

"I heerd that wee girl your after went home with the new man in the fish factory Hughie",

Stanley said as he reached upward with his brush to catch the underside of the rail.

"If she did then she would lose the ring ah bought her yesterday and she's no sae stupid."

Hughie had learnt that there was no malice in Stanley and that he was really giving him the opportunity to tell his workmates the news he was bursting to tell anyway. They all congratulated him warmly, continuing to apply the bright blue paint to the hull.

Another boat drew into the dock and began unloading box after box of prawns. Reuben counted sixty boxes swinging on to the pier and as it was morning he deduced the boat had been fishing all night.

"You've been fishing Dundalk Bay then",

he shouted at the youngest crewman. The lad was eager to confirm Reuben's guess, much to the chagrin of the boat's skipper who knew full well that Reuben would finish painting up and be off the Dundalk Bay that night. Reuben attacked the painting with renewed vigour urging the others to greater efforts.

Hughie let his paint brush fall as he reached to cover a plank that was really beyond his stretch. The brush fell into the dock, Hugh bent his knee to retrieve it and at that moment Aaron shifted his weight to the right leg at the back of the plank. The plank was now unbalanced and flipped over pitching the four men into the dock.

The dock was nine foot deep and the crew of the *"Star of Hope"* encumbered as they were by their sea boots became stuck in the viscous mud at the bottom.

By the time the crew of the trawler alongside had rushed aboard their boat with ropes and lifebelt all four had drowned standing up in nine feet of water. They still talk about Reuben Foy in Killglass, the risks he took, the money he earned and the ridiculously tragic end he and his courageous crew took.

A Destiny for Joe

A Destiny for Joe

Joseph Hughes was a Belfast Catholic. Brian Moore has described the condition of a Belfast Catholic as akin to that of a Jew anywhere else. Joe had read Brian Moore and couldn't see this at all. He put it down to the fact that Brian Moore, also a Belfast Catholic, lived on the Antrim Road, then a fashionable residential area with a sizeable Jewish population, whereas he Joe lived in the Markets district, a notoriously deprived ghetto area. To Joe a Jewish person was very privileged indeed, usually a businessman or a doctor or a lawyer. Joe's father owned a small terrace of kitchen houses in one of which the Hughes family dwelled and by the standards of the district they were relatively well off, in that they always had shoes on their feet and food on the table.

Through his father's connections Joe got an apprenticeship to the joinery trade when he left school and this again set him above the level of his pals in the district who mostly did lumpen jobs in the markets or on building sites. Due to his attendance at trade classes at the technical college, Joe, for the first time, came into contact with Protestant youths. The jobbing builder, for whom he worked, was a friend of his father's and only employed Catholics. For young men like Joe, at the end of the Second World War, the main social life was the gathering of the men at the steet corner. The main topic of conversion was the late war and the returned ex-servicemen would always be given the floor as they recalled their exploits in foreign lands. The younger men would be infuenced by American war films and debate at a safe distance the relative fighting qualities of the American marines and the Japanese Imperial Army. Now that the war was over Joe often felt that there must be other areas of human adventurous interest in the world.

He used to read avidly the magazine "Wide World" whose contents consisted of allegedly true life adventures by intrepid explorers, deep sea divers, gold prospectors and the like. Joe determined to see some of this wide world as soon as he earned his first journeyman's wage. One of the youths who gathered at the corner was learning Gaelic and as he seemed more intelligent than the rest, Joe started to read Irish history to equip himself for the endless debates this particular youth would initiate. This eventually led to a brief connection with the Fianna, the youth wing of the IRA. It seemed at the time to be a better way of passing the time than standing at the corner. Every Sunday Joe and his Gaelic speaking friend took the bus to the Carr's Glen where a wild eyed youth with pimples shouted shrill commands at them in Gaelic, left turn, right turn, form fours, for hours on end. The senior terrorists obviously did not trust the Fianna with anything more dangerous. Eventually this seemed a pointless thing to be at and Joe just stopped going.

Five years passed and Joe became a competent carpenter, if not a very exact craftsman, lifted his first journeyman's wage and with it his employment cards.

He bought himself an ex-army rucksack and sleeping bag and was on the Liverpool boat that night. His destination was uncertain, somewhere south certainly, towards the sun and sea. A week later he presented himself to the foreman of a building site on the outskirts of Paris. He showed him his set of joiner's tools and was taken on, all through sign language. The language question was not important. Joe knew what was to be done and got on with it. French workers at the time were sympathetic to English speaking foreigners and proved to be interested in questions of wages and conditions in Britain.

Soon Joe had several hundreds of francs saved, enough to move south to the sea and the sun. In these months he kept his own company indulging himself only in a bottle of Beaujolais and a packet of Gauloises. A book on astral navigation provided his only company. Wandering round Cannes harbour, he observed the luxurious ocean going yachts whose graceful lines impressed him greatly. The opulance of the craft overwhelmed him but not enough to stop him knowing that the owners of these beautiful craft were no seamen. Once he spotted an elegant craft registered in Belfast and he wondered who was rich enough to own it.

One day while admiring an ocean going yacht, he fell into conversation with the cockney skipper. It transpired that the boat which was registered in Panama, belonged to an American millionaire who spent his time cruising the Mediterranean. It appeared that there was a vacancy for an AB/cook and Joe was delighted to take the job. Millionaire or not, the American did not pay very well. Ten dollars a week was all that was on offer, but apparently little work was involved as the owner spent most of his time ashore and pin money could be made selling duty free cigarettes.

They sailed that night for Tangiers, Joe taking his watch on the wheel and trying to make conversation with a definitely monosyllabic American. Conversation came easy to Joe, it being the chief form of recreation of his youth, but he found that conversation with the American was more difficult than with his former French work mates. It soon became apparent that the American was engaged in smuggling duty free cigarettes from Tangiers to France but this didn't bother Joe too much. He cooked adequate meals for four and stood his watch. He bought a theodolite, practised navigation and kept his own counsel. Sometimes women came on board with the American and Joe was required to cook a meal for them. The cockney said they were business girls, a euphemism for high class prostitutes. They all seemed so posh to him. He met one in Naples one night and he brought her back on board. She demanded and got ten dollars but the whole transaction to Joe was very commercial and altogether very unsatisfactory.

There was a strange atmosphere on the yacht with everybody knowing about the smuggling and yet nobody mentioning it. The twin topics of conversation were the state of the sea and the price of stores and cigarettes. Years later in Belfast, in the era of arms shipments and its allied trade of drugs dealing, it all seemed to Joe to be a bit ridiculous.

Joe had taken this drifting life in his stride, his fulfillment being to sit on deck on a starlit night contenting himself with a bottle of wine and a Gauloise. Faraway from the constrictions of the Belfast Catholic milieu it had been easy to adandon formal religion and the world now made a sort of sense to him. He felt at one with the elements, more spiritual than ever he felt sitting through a gabbled Latin Mass. Here where the sea met the sky, where the moon gleamed and the morse-code fickering stars guided, nature was God, and so it should be, Joe felt.

During the passage to Cannes from Tangiers one trip, they had an engine breakdown. They wallowed about a lumpy sea for a while and eventually the engineer coaxed three knots from the engine and they limped into Malaga. The Malaga drydock was in many ways like Harland and Wolff in the sun, not withstanding the strange language, sounds and smells. Having a trade in common with the Spanish shipwrights, Joe would sometimes lift an adze and shape a plank which he would hold forth for the inspection of the Spaniards. This established a bond between them giving rise to invitations to join them in their Friday night carousals at the dockside bar. Soon however their English would run out and Joe would be left alone with his thoughts. Through these contacts he found that their working life was much the same as the life of a Belfast joiner. He regretted bitterly the time he spent trying to master the dead Gaelic language and leaving his head deaf and dumb to this musical language that flowed all round him in Spain. The Spanish workers were proud men and proud of their work, badly paid as it was. As a good trademan this is what Joe found to be missing in the life of a luxury yacht sailor.

After a year Joe decided to go home so when the yacht docked in Genoa he lifted his wages, caught the train to Paris and then on to Dover, Liverpool and Belfast.

He settled down in the family home in Belfast and was regarded as footloose and irresponsible by his family and as an oddity by his peers. The lack of privacy in the small Markets house irked him. His sisters all wanted to bath when he needed a shave it seemed to him.

Then he started to court a girl with a thirty-eight inch bust, found her physically stimulating, so he decided to wed out of fustration. The girl's father lent him the deposit for a kitchen house further up the road in what later became known as a religiously mixed district. At that time it was not the religious mix that mattered but the mix between the owner-occupiers and the protected seven-shillings-a-week tenants. The tenants were generally older people who had their rents fixed between the wars when inflation was unknown. Joe and his bride worked with a will to improve their new home, fitting up a bath in the spare bedroom, pulling out the Aga range to fit a new Devon grate. Two decades later would find suede-coated ladies bidding furiously at auctions for the privilege of owning an Aga range. Later the bath had to be dismantled to make a bedroom for an expanding brood.

Six years and four children later, Joe's wife's bust measured forty-four inches and her waist thirty-eight and she had lost all interest in sexual activity. Joe ranted, raved and even offered violence, all to no avail, so he lost interest in the house.

During the week when his money had run out, he would sit in the small parlour taking imaginary sights with this sextant, perusing books on sailing and navigation with desultory interest. Sometimes he would sip from a bottle of South African fortified wine and look out at the smoke grey street wondering what made him return to this loveless gloomy city. He could have married a Spanish or Italian woman who would have set him on a pedestal in the sun. Instead he was maladjusted to the lack of sex, living a hostile truce with his wife and suffering the contempt of his growing children. The carefully selected furniture was now chipped and broken, the prize Devon grate missing tiles.

On the building sites where he worked, pornographic magazines circulated freely and sometimes Joe would bring one home and retire to his lonely pleasures in the parlour.

His wife reproached him for his lack of ambition, his drinking and, it seemed to him, for his very existence.

"Call yourself a tradesman. Look at this house, like a midden it is. Look at my brother, out on his own with four men working for him. Lovely house on the Antrim Road too."

This hectoring infuriated Joe as he knew that her brother, an electrician, couldn't tell a positive from a negative but had the ability to convince his customers that they were getting a bargain as he overcharged them.

One day the eldest boy came home in the uniform of the Army Cadet Force. Joe fumed and cursed him and the lad wrongly thought it was the British uniform that upset him but Joe saw in the army uniform the perversity of his children's desire to thwart him. Why could the skitter not have joined the Sea Cadets and share something with his father?

A year later when the boy left school he took a job washing cars in a garage and refused to take up an apprenticeship his father had secured for him in the building firm.

"I see too much of my Da as it is. I don't want him breathing down my neck at work."

After that Joe washed his hands of his son.

Then the anti-partition riots came bringing with them tensions between Catholic and Protestant workers. Joe clung always to a rough philosophy that working people should always stick together against the bosses but the nationalist tide swept away all independent thought. One night the tensions errupted with a vengeance when a shower of bricks and bottles smashed through Joe's window. The eldest son arrived panting at the back door simultaneously having to run all the way from the top of the Ormeau Road where he had been taunted by Protestant youths from the nearby estate. The family cowered in the back bedroom as the cries of

"Fenian Bastards"
were interspersed with the sound of breaking glass. Eventually the police arrived and dispersed the mob leaving Joe's family in an insecure peace. Joe blamed it on the boy for shouting back at the Protestant youths and then letting them follow him home. The next time it happened, Joe borrowed a van, moved his family and battered furniture and then squatted in a high rise flat in the Catholic heartland of the lower Falls road.

The high rise block was new at the time, the lifts worked and the flat had three bedrooms which afforded a spendid view across the city to the Belfast Lough and the rolling Castlereagh Hills beyond. It became known as the Planet of the IRSP's because of the activities of a murder gang who self styled themselves as the Irish Republican Socialist Party and who based themselves in the high rise. Often there were murder bids on police and army patrols or even on disgruntled gang members. On a clear night Joe often sat in his bedroom practising taking sights with his sextant.

One night while sitting in the dark trying to get a fix on the North Star he heard the crack of a rifle shot followed by the stacatto sound of automatic rifle fire. This was the Provos or the IRSP's having a go at the army he thought. Then inside the room "ping thud thud ping." He flattened on the floor as two bullets imbedded in the wall behind him. Next he heard the thumping of feet, shouted curses and the crashing of rifle butts against the door as the lock gave way and the Paras burst into the room with shouts of "On the fucking floor."

As Joe was already on the floor he was at a loss to know what to do, so he held up the sextant with his right arm.

The Paras had no idea what the sextant was and it took some time to convince them it was an instrument for navigation.

"Fucking stupid thing to be at in the middle of a tower block,"
the sergeant said.

"Lucky you're alive Paddy. One of our men was winged by them bastards and we see this geyser squinting through a sight at us in a darkened room."
It was no longer safe in Belfast even to use your imagination.

The first night his son came home drunk Joe was furious. His remonstrances met with derision from the sixteen year old boy so he drew his fist back to strike the lad when the boy turned on him, belabouring his father with blows that brought him to his knees, bleeding from his nose and mouth. Joe's mind filled with the biblical imprecation,

"Well done thy good and faithful servant. Thy reward shall be in heaven," as he struggled to his feet.

Joe did not intend to wait that long for his reward so when a cheque for £1,000 arrived from the Housing Executive, the proceeds of the sale of his house, he bought an airline ticket for New York where he had an aunt. With the first glimpse of New York from the taxi window Joe knew that he had left it too late at fortyseven to settle in his bustling city. His aunt was a single lady approaching sixty who worked in Bloomingdales and who intended to return to Belfast to draw her pension where she hoped she would be less lonely than in New York. She was glad to have her eldest sister's son for company but Joe found it irksome living in someone else's house. He socialised in a nearby Irish pub but although he could have got work through the Irish grapevine he knew that he could never afford the rent of an apartment in Manhatten. It was all too bewildering, the flashing neons the rushing pedestrians of so many colours and the general rudeness of everybody.

A month went by so when his money was all but gone he bought a ticket back to Belfast.

As far as his wife and family were concerned Joe might never been away. His wife got as much from the social security as he had been able to give her and she never wanted him for anything else.

The eldest boy had fallen into bad company, involved himself in petty crime then been tortured by the IRA enforcers whom he promptly joined. Then he was caught by the police acting as lookout for an attempted assassination of a postman who was a part-time soldier. Joe's wife now spent her time between excursions to the prison and excursions to the bingo hall.

Belfast city centre was now cordoned off and likened to a graveyard with traffic lights. The ubiquitous soldiers who had little idea what they were doing or for whom to look, became part of the streetscape.

Intercommunal tensions made it difficult for Joe to work outside Catholic areas so he drew social security and did the odd repair job on the side. Mostly he sat in his bedroom gazing across the roofs at the hills beyond.

A Destiny for Joe

One drizzly Saturday morning a sea of banners glided into his view and slowly moved down the Falls road. There was something different about the five thousand strong crowd that bore them. Not so strident perhaps as the usual ranting republican demonstrations that occurred frequently. He rushed down the stairs to witness the demonstrators who were mostly middle aged and mostly women who moved with dignified solemnity. He could now read the banners "Andersonstown for peace", "Ormeau Road Peace People", "Shankill Community Centre for Peace" and similar geographically based slogans. This was the first demonstration of the new peace movement of which Joe had heard talk. Now cautious in their newly found strength they moved with growing confidence. In the main they were silent, engaging only in the brittle embarrassed conversation of self-consious people unused to public exposure. There was some hostility from passers by, mostly from juveniles who shouted "Brit lovers". The women, terrified they would be attacked, huddled together and clasped each other's hands but still kept moving. Joe joined the procession as it turned into Northhumberland Street, heading towards the Shankill Road. This the Protestant heartland of West Belfast, once a hub of commercial activity but now depleted of its people by the social engineers, had not seen Joe Hughes since August 1969 when he had collected his tool box from his employer's yard before slinking down the road with his cap pulled down over his eyes.

The Shankill was crowded with shoppers some of whom seemed paralysed with amazement. Others overcome with emotion reached out to embrace the peace marchers. Joe, recognising a familiar face, experienced a moment of panic. The atavistice cry of "Fenian Bastard" rang out and Joe prepared to run for his life. Fortunately the cry eminated from the shaven skull of a teenager in jeans and not from the familiar face.

The march ended with a meeting harangued by speakers with pious words which meant nothing to Joe.

"Just ould slabbering"

he murmured to himself. What did mean something was to walk up the Shankill where he used to work and to conquer the fear that he had felt. That had meant something to him. When the meeting ended he walked home with a throng of other people back up to the Falls Road high rises. Over the peace line the ubiquitous soldiers walked about scanning the skyline, chirping into the microphones on their flak jackets. A strange form of talking to yourself Joe thought. He often talked to himself these days.

As he entered the stairwell of the high rise he thought of all the hundreds of women living in this so called street in the sky, surely there is some woman somewhere who wants a good man in her bed. In the kitchen his wife only paused from her cooking long enough to berate him so he went down to the off licence, purchased a bottle of Tawney wine which with six tins of beer and a fish supper was his evening meal.

The next morning the sun shone with a crystal clear light only found in Ireland. Joe took the bus to Ardglass on the County Down coast. The sea in the harbour there was flat calm and the hottest sun he had ever felt in Ireland filtered through the heat haze. Just before noon the mist scattered and Joe standing on the harbour wall lifted his sextant and took sight on the noonday sun. Satisfied, he walked to the pub at the end of the pier and drank a cool pint of lager. He caught the barman's eye as he lifted the glass to his mouth. "To peace," he said.

The barman nodded and said

"To peace."

The Patriarch

The Patriarch

It was the summer of 1965 when I sat down in the London tube, avoiding eye contact as everyone does and looking forward to seeing my son at his house in Hampstead. I am retired now, after a lifetime in the service of the Hibernian Bank in the West and North of Ireland, with periodic visits to London to break the long winter of life in the seaside town near Belfast which is now my home. I was scanning the latest advertisements on the wall of the train when my ears picked up the soft tones of a West of Ireland brogue. It was a grey haired woman on the opposite seat talking to her younger companion. I narrowed the location of the accent to those of County Clare and emboldened by my own perception I ventured a conversational query.

"Are you from the banner county then?"

The woman hesitated while she appraised me and smiled.

"Indeed I am but I am here a long time. I am from Kilkeshen originally but I never go back now."

The name Kilkeshen struck a chord in my psyche as I had spent my first two years of service in the bank there at a very turbulent time in the early twenties.

"I lived in Kilkeshen myself, my name is Maxwell. I was the junior clerk in the Hibernian Bank in 1921. May I ask what your name is?"

"We were Crangles. My father was the station sergeant in the RIC. There are none of us there now."

I looked more closely at the two women and a frisson of recognition entered my head and brought me back to that bleak village in County Clare 45 years ago. In the older woman's domed forehead, creased with worry lines, plus the ice blue eyes I saw the commanding visage of Sergeant Crangle, my bridge partner in those far off troubled times of my youth. I saw Crangle too in the younger woman and I knew her now to be his grandchild.

"I knew your father well",

I said.

"Does he live still?"

"No, my father died ten years ago in Banbridge in Northern Ireland where he moved after the treaty. He was the head constable there. The children are scattered over England and America."

I knew by the set of her mouth that the woman had known much trouble and had taxed her strength to overcome it. I dropped my voice to commiserate.

"I am sorry to hear that but it does not surprise me that he became a head constable. He was a very conscientious policeman."
"Indeed he was, too concientious,"
said the woman,
"Miriam here is my daughter. She never saw her grandfather."
Sergeant Crangle had seven children and I now knew that this woman was the youngest, Bridgeen.
I had arrived in Kilkeshen in twenty-one when the guerilla war with its ambushes and atrocities was at its height. The bank manager's first question to me was to ascertain my competence at bridge, advising me that between the pendulum of boredom and fear it was the only thing that kept him sane. Indeed most of the time the village was quiet as the grave and I soon learnt that the back room in Considine's Hotel, where I had my lodgings, was the only place where any sort of social intercourse took place. There was a bridge school there every Friday night where the bank manager, the police sergeant and the school principal could play and have a quiet drink away from the public bar. My predecessor had been the fourth player and now I was expected to fill his place.
The work in the bank was not taxing, most days past with less than twenty transactions, mostly with the "Merchant Princes" of the village, as my boss called the few hucksters and publicans who managed to eke out an existence in the place. The village itself was one long street of grey stone cottages with rotting thatches, with five spirit grocers, the hotel, the police barracks and the railway station giving the place its reason for existence. A Catholic church and two-room school had been built at the end of the village after the repeal of the penal laws. There was a company of Scottish soldiers stationed in the police barracks to give added protection to the six Royal Irish Constabulary men and their families and for counter insurgency duties in the low hills behind the village. At night caged lorries known as Crossley tenders, could be heard rumbling through the village bearing the soldiers and police out on patrol to search for "shinners" as the Sinn Fein rebels were known. On such a night, as I made my way to Considine's after work, I first saw Sergeant Crangle. He sat bolt upright beside the military driver in the lead tender. His peaked cap sat straight on his head so that the shiny visor practically obscured his vision. His piercing blue eyes and waxed grey moustache were all

that was discernable above the well pressed bottle green tunic that sported the King's Police Medal ribbon. Across his knees he nursed a carbine. The manager told me that as station sergeant he didn't have to go on patrol but he felt it his duty to lead his men. It was said he was fearless under fire and that the shinners had vowed to shoot him before the year was out. The shinners had put out a boycott decree on the police and military but Mrs Considine avoided it by opening the side door of the hotel to admit Sergeant Crangle. The Scottish soldiers often had trysts with the village girls on the roads and loanens beyond the village. It was said that the parish priest could be seen walking the roads after dark looking for the sight of tartan and bare flesh in the ditches. If the priest found a courting couple he would roust them out with his blackthorn stick and the unlucky girl would take off over the fields lest she would be recognised. Certainly some of the soldiers were Gaelic speaking Catholics from the Hebrides and had much in common with the locals and indeed when they left Kilkeshan for India several of the village girls went with them. The manager taught me the rudiments of bridge during the day and would sometimes ring the alarm bell thus signalling Considine's pot boy to bring two bottles of stout to the bank. Thus prepared I presented myself to the side door of Considine's on Friday night and met Sergeant Crangle for the first time. He sat at the table in the back room resplendant in high white starched collar, his serge blue suiting pressed with knife edge creases and a gold watch and chain across his narrow stomach. The broad domed forehead was topped by iron grey cropped hair. His eyes were piercing blue set off by black bushy eyebrows. When he stood to be introduced to me I could see his was all of six-foot-three and had a military bearing that demanded respect and obedience. With his regular nose and strong chin in another age he could have been a romantic lead in a cowboy or gangster film and no doubt the very idea would have appalled him. He spoke with the accent of west Cork and told me he had served in Armagh in the North of Ireland where he met and married his wife. The other player was the quiet soft spoken school master who was from Dublin and hated every minute he spent in Kilkeshen.

We played bridge for two hours in silent contemplation, then relaxing over pints of stout a convivial conversation flowed. The school teacher bemoaned his herculean task, as he put it.

"Of inculcating respect for learning in the minds or bog peasants destined for the digging of ditches or looking up the plough horse's arse to the end of their days."
He had a new assistant who was an enthusiastic Irish language revivalist, "spouting Gaelic out of his arse,"
the teacher said.
"Irish never buttered any parsnips. It's good English, mathmatics and science are the keys to success in life."
"My father and mother spoke Irish,"
the sergeant said.
"But they always spoke to me in English for which I am grateful otherwise I would never have got the police exam. They spoke to the brother in Irish all right but he was going to get the farm and wouldn't need a great knowledge of English."
It became clear to me that I was only tolerated for my hand at bridge and as far as the conversation went I was ignored. I then realised that these men were outsiders, they were not of the village, their loyalties lay elsewhere and that their friendship was tempered in the fires of mutal support against the hostility that was directed towards them.
On Sunday the thirty or so Scottish soldiers who were Catholics marched to the church from the barracks while the Protestants went in their Crossley tenders to the Protestant church in the next village. In the Catholic church which I then attended, I was surprised to find that the male parishioners sat at one side of the church while the females sat at the other. The kilted soldiers sat at two rows at the back. I was again surprised to see Sergeant Crangle in his police uniform, bearing his ceremonial spiked helmet under his arm, march up the aisle followed by his wife and three of his children. He ignored the rule of separate seating and occupied a pew together with his family on the men's side. Two parishioners sheepishly slid along the pew and moved to another seat. Such was the fear of the shinners boycott that even in the house of God it could not be breached. From where I was sitting I could see Crangle's broad black back and beside him the dark shoulder length tresses of his youngest daughter. A young man slipped into the seat beside me. He was small, dark and had an air of intensity confirmed by the gold ring of the Irish speakers Fainne in his lapel. His dark brooding eyes were shielded by wire

framed round glasses. Without being told I knew this to be the new assistant school teacher that had been referred to at the bridge night. The priest faced the altar to pour the wine and at that moment Crangle's youngest daughter quickly turned her head and showed her beautiful face to me. Here blue eyes flashed for a second and then she turned away. She would have been about fifteen years old but there was an air of worldliness about them that said she was in the full of ripeness of womanhood. An almost imperceptive stirring from the young man beside me alerted me to the fact that the flashing eyes were directed not to me but to my neighbour. The Mass over, the kilted soldiers formed up outside and marched off to the command of a sergeant followed by some ribald shouts from the more loutish inhabitants of the village. The worshippers remained clustered in conversational knots around the forecourt of the chapel as was the custom of people from the outlying farms who rarely saw each other during the week. I spoke to the schoolmaster and we were joined by my erstwhile neighbour who was indeed the new assistant at the school.

"Caid dia mara ta tu"

was his Gaelic response to my introduction from his boss. His name was Michael Vesey and I perceived the light of a true fanatic in his eyes.

As we talked, Sergeant Crangle dismounted the steps of the church followed by his wife and three children. He was ramrod straight, his spiked helmet gave him the appearance of even greater height as he strode across the church yard as if oblivious to the knots of country folk. The schoolmaster and myself greeted him civilly as he passed with his entourage and received a half salute by way of response. I noted however that Michael Vesey averted his eyes and involuntarily shifted from one foot to the other. The youngest daughter's passage however caused him to turn and face her and when he was inches from her his hand was surreptitiously reached to hers in a brief but intimate encounter. Vesey had turned his face to attend the conversation in the presumption that his clandestine contact with the girl would not be noticed, but noticed it was by both the master and myself. The knots of worshippers gradually dispersed giving Vesey his excuse to leave and as he did, I saw that he walked with a limp.

"He's a bit spavined for a young man",

I observed to the master.

"Yes, he hurt his leg playing bogball I believe."
Bogball was the Dublinman's peroritive term for the Gaelic form of football which was being revived at the time.
That night at dusk three Crossley tenders swung out of the barrack gate and slowly crawled up the road towards the Clare hills. Crangle as usual was in the lead vehicle and was first to be hit when a fusillade of .303 bullets shattered the windscreen as the column passed the turf stack at Crohaun cross roads. The IRA gunmen were concealed behind the turf stack and in the ditch at the other side of the road. Clutching his shattered arm Sergeant Crangle shouted.
"Dismount and return fire!"
The lorry halted with the driver now dead and slumpled over the wheel, blood spurting through a hole in his Scottish bonnet. The soldiers flung themselves from the lorries and assumed firing positions, taking what cover they could by the Crossley wheels and by the side of the ditches.
"Shoot through the turf stack,"
Crangle shouted.
"The bastards are behind it."
Single aimed shots were coming from the shinners in the ditch and their noise was punctuated by the groans of the wounded soldiers. Some of the soldiers in the rear lorry had managed to set up a Lewis machine gun and were now raking the turf stack with automatic fire. The rat-tat-tat sound plus the flashing muzzle heartened the soldiers who were now breaking cover and running in an encircling formation, firing from the hip. The shinners, about fifteen of them, broke from behind the turf stack and fled across the bog. Sergeant Crangle was the first man to reach the turf stack in time to see the last of the gunmen broach the horizon. The gunman cut a small figure and as he ran in a hopskip kind of motion he turned and fired with a revolver and then disappeared. Crangle fired his revolver with his left hand but it was more of a parting gesture than an aimed shot.
The soldiers did not pursue the fleeing gunmen but mustered behind the last Crossley to take stock. The lead driver was dead and there was three wounded including one RIC man. Behind the turfstack they found cigarette butts and empty cartridge cases. There was also blood on the ground indicating that the Lewis gun rounds had penetrated the turf stack and that one or more of

the shinners were wounded.

One of the Highlanders was wounded in the stomach and was groaning piti-fully. He was a youth of about eighteen from Glasgow whose pimply face was contorted with pain. The corporal had pressed a field dressing to the wound to staunch the bood but it was now seeping through both the dressing and the rough serge khaki cloth of his tunic.

"Help me for Christ sake or a willna see ma mither again."

"Be a brave sodger the noo. W'eel hae ye in the hospital soon,"

the corporal comforted him.

The young soldier died in agony on the bumping Crossly tender on the way to Ennis Hospital. Sergeant Crangle's forearm was smashed and was set in plaster of Paris after the bullet was extracted, leaving him in considerable pain. The two dead soldiers were coffined and sent in a military lorry to Dublin and then placed on the ferry for Glasgow where they were buried with full military honours. There were numerous raids on IRA suspects in the area but all of them had alibis and no incriminating articles were found.

Among the houses searched was a farmhouse of the outskirts of the village where the new assistant teacher Michael Vesey took his lodgings. It was a low stone thatched cottage with a muddy yard and a mud floor with hens running in and out. Small children played among the turf stacks and the pig midden. Sergeant Crangle, although on sick leave, went along with the police raiding party. They searched the thatch and midden with long probes but found nothing. Vesey arrived back during the search and Crangle asked him what he new about the raid. Vesey refused to answer in English, insisting on using the Connaught dialect of Gaelic that he had learned. Crangle, who un-derstood only Munster Irish, could make no headway.

Crangle's face was red with rage. He knew that if he arrested the school-teacher the Bishop would make representations to the authorities and have him released in a day and he would be reprimanded for exceeding his authority.

"You know English well enough to read the writing on the pound notes you collect every month from the government",

he shouted.

The young man's face was steely and impassive, confident in his own con-viction and probity, showing neither contempt or fear.

Over the next few weeks the village resumed its sleeply atmosphere, nobody mentioned the deaths at the cross roads except the Scots soldiers who were embittered by the deaths of their comrades. They never smiled now or greeted the locals although there were still trysts in the boreens and bushes with the local girls. As most of the girls would eventually go to America they cared little what their fathers or brothers thought. At the Friday night bridge game I noticed that the normally taciturn Sergeant Crangle, who sat with this tunic draped over his wounded arm, had his eyes lit up with an unnatural brightness. He berated the rebels for needlessly plunging the country into war for what was never achievable.

"These Gaelic-spouting amadans don't know the North. The people there will never come into a united Ireland. Eventually the shinners will settle for what's on offer. In the meantime they are drowning the country in blood."

He stated this to the schoolmaster whom he half suspected of knowing something about the republican associations of Michael Vesey who had now disappeared.

Some weeks later on a winters night when a south-westerly gale howled round the hills and rattled the window sashes in the Kilkeshen cottages, the apprentice teacher Vesey appeared at the side door of the barrack. He demanded of the soldier on guard that he speak to the police sergeant. When Crangle appeared from his quarters clad in vest and police trousers, he looked at Vesey with contempt, told him to wait and returned with his tunic buttoned to the neck. Beside him Vesey looked weedy and dishevelled. They went to the day room where Crangle sat behind the desk, his stare fixed on the green and dun barrack wall. Photographs of wanted insurgents competed for space with notices concerning warble fly and ragwort. Crangle nodded to the poster of Dan Breen wanted for the murder of a policeman near Sligo.

"I suppose you would know this man. He murdered my best friend in cold blood."

"I know nothing of that but I want to tell you something that will be to your advantage but it is not in my interest to relate it."

"Then why tell it to me then,"

the sergeant countered.

"We will come to that later but just now I want your assurance that you will not divulge anything of which I speak to another mortal soul." Vesey said this with his face drained of colour as if angry and frightened at the same time. The sergeant bristled visibly, his eyes flashed and then he stood up.

"I draw my pay so I will do my duty as I see fit so it you have anything to tell me tell it",

said the sergeant looking down on him.

"I know more about you than you think. That you were seen at the ambush where the two kilties were corpsed and I was winged and I know your are in a so-called active service unit about the business of shooting policemen."

"And you are about the business of shooting sparrows I suppose", countered the teacher.

"I will tell you what I have to tell you and if you breathe a word to a living soul I'll come looking for you."

The sergeant, unused to any verbal defiance, was taken aback and sat down and with a deft turn of his palm indicated to the teacher to say his piece.

"I am suggesting that you and your family be out of the barrack on Saturday night."

The sergeant stared hard at the teacher.

"What you are saying is that there will be an attack on Saturday night and that I should desert my post and save myself and my family. Now I must ask why are you giving me this information?"

The teacher's dark visage flushed and in a voice quivering with anger he slowly and carefully explained that he was no informer and that he loved the sergeant's youngest daughter Bridgeen and that he wanted to marry her, so for that reason only he wanted her and her family to escape the bloodletting that would ensue. The effect of this declaration was explosive. Crangle's face reddened, his eyes widened and flashed and with an oath he seized the small schoolteacher by the shoulders and frog-marched him out of the day room, past the startled soldiers in the guardroom from where he heaved him bodily into the street.

"Don't you ever see my daughter again you treacherous Mayo Scoundrel," was his parting shot to Michael Vesey.

All of this of course was unknown to me at the time and I learned of it only after the attack on the barracks the following Saturday night. The memory of that attack is forever burned into my mind. The bank manager, who was on close terms with the sergeant, had learned to respect the confidences of his friends as well as of his customers. He did not however appraise me of Vesey's warning to the sergeant until long after the attack. Bridgeen left the barracks of the Friday night never to see her father again. Her father gave her an ultimatum, in spite of Mrs Crangle's pleading, either never to see Vesey again or to pack her bags and go. Certainly nobody in the village ever knew the end taken by Michael Vesey and Bridgeen Crangle.

Some days later my own peaceful routine was rudely shattered by the sudden appearance of a middle-aged kilted soldier in the shape of Company Sergeant-Major McPherson in my room at 4 pm. He was a stocky well-built man dressed in battle gear with ammunition pouches and steel helmet. A canvas apron covered his kilt. He carried a .303 rifle over his shoulder. His waxed mustaches and rows of medal ribbons attested to a long and successful military career. He had dark hair and that swarthy skin Scotsmen sometimes have, along with a very Scottish button nose.

"Sorry to disturb you laddie but under martial law I have to detain you here until further notice. I have rations here for the two of us so you'll no be needin' your tea."

I had never thought much about politics and only then as it affected myself. I only wanted the troubles to be over, whatever the settlement and to be able to get on with my career in the bank as my father had done in the civil service. Now however I felt great resentment that this military Scotsman could order me to stay in my room where I paid the rent.

"What do you want here",

I riposted with some anger.

"I have nothin to do with the shinners. Ask the RIC sergeant."

"I already have",

replied the Sergeant-Major.

"He said you wouldn't make a fuss. You see laddie, your room overlooks the barracks and we expect an attack, so we need to keep you here to make sure the rebels aren'y warned."

I realised then that my position was precarious and I would like as not be shot if a gun battle took place. I abandoned my plans to go to the Saturday night picture show and settled down to share whatever fate had in store for the sergeant-major and my unwilling self.

The sergeant-major positioned himself beside the window with his rifle lying up again the corner. Before placing the rifle there, he had worked the bolt and I presumed this action made it ready to fire. He then took some cartridge clips out from his pouches and laid them in neat order beside him on the floor. The sight of the polished wooden stock of the rifle and the bullets on the floor filled my with raw revulsion and apprehension. It was something grossly alien to me, bringing the imminent danger of bloodshed and death into the room. I was always timid as a child and preferred childish fantasies to the rough games of soldiers and football that the other boys played. Because of this I attended to my studies and easily passed the bank entrance examinations. Now I found myself central to a conflict in a rain-soaked benighted village in the west of Ireland. In my predicament the prospect of emigration to the colonies or indeed to Amercia where so many of the Clare people fled. The sergeant-major broke my reverie by offering me a corned beef sandwich and a bottle of stout.

"Nae beer for me laddie",
he said as he swigged from the water bottle.
"Ah mun keep a guid eeye in ma heid which is why ah'm here. I hae allus been the best shot in the battalion. Dinna fash yoursell laddie when ah shoot there'll be nae shot back."
I pondered on these observations and wondered on the nature of a military society where a man was judged by the straightness of his aim. I asked him his reasons for joining the army and why he and stayed in it for so long. He explained that he was the eldest son of a miner's ten children from Lanarkshire and he had seen his father a broken aged man at forty and had thought it better to take a chance on a early death in the army. The lack of privacy was no hardship for him after sharing a two-room miner's cottage with twelve people.

"I got three square meals a day and nae worry if I would be laid off like feyther. Baith ma lads are in A company in Ennis and ma dochter is marrit til a sodger in the Cameronians in Germany."
He retailed this without taking his eye off the barrack door.
"Aifter the Kyber Pass and Flanders this show in Ireland is Nae bother."
Twilight closed in on the village and with it an uneasy quietness. Horse and

donkey carts disappeared from the street and the half doors which were open were closed and bolted.

"These folk ken fine weel there's a raid on",

offered the sergeant-major.

I felt this to be true but unable to give voice to the thought on the grounds that I would be stigmatising my own people with cunning complicity in an assassination.

"Everything goes quiet about this time on a Saturday night, Mr McPherson. It is just the break before the Saturday night carousel. Look! There's a tinker's cart coming down the street."

A traditional tinker's covered wagon pulled by a piebald pony was being driven by a dark-haired man with a red kerchief round his neck. As the cart approached I could see the driver wore an old British army tunic with the badges of the Connaught Rangers on the collar. The Connaught Rangers had many volunteers from the travelling community in the recent war so there was nothing incongruous about this. A battered sweat-stained trilby hat was perched on the back of his head and he puffed on a clay pipe. I looked at McPherson whose mouth was slightly open and whose eyes were still narrowed but yet he seemed far away in this thoughts.

The sergeant-major was thinking of the thousands of hours he must have spent during his army service keeping watch. His regiment 'The Black Watch', were well named he thought. He had watched the empty wintry Scottish night on sentry duty as a recruit at the depot. He had watched the barren rocks on the Indian north-west frontier as a young soldier, watching for the slightest movement that might herald an attack by the Pathans. For four years in the Great War as an NCO he had watched the teenage soldiers in the trenches for signs of panic or carelessness that could cause an abrupt end to their young lives by a sniper's bullet or a death sentence by court martial for desertion. The old soldier's adage that if you weren't fighting you were marching should be changed to "or watching."

I broke his reverie by asking him if he felt a loyalty to King and country.

"No"

he replied.

"I hae no love for the King or his feyther afore him or his auld granmither. Like the poet Kipling said."

Then he tipped his chin in the air as if mentally switching from Broad Scots to English.

"Walk wide o' the widow o' Windsor

for it's half o' creation she owns.

And we bought her the same with the sword and the flame

And we salted it down with our bones."

The barrack door was solid oak, green painted, locked and barred, seldom used now as a new wall and gate had been erected to the handball alley which was now used for parking Crossley tenders. This was not visible from the main street and was safer from ambush. The sergeant-major slowly adopted the firing position, quietly ordering me to get under the bed. Strangely I was no longer frightened and ignored him in order to witness whatever would occur.

As the tinker's cart passed the barrack door the driver jumped from his seat and pulled a bundle from under his tunic. The pony halted as the driver puffed vigourously on his clay pipe which he then applied to what appeared to be a string attached to the bundle. The string spluttered and sparked. It was cordite. At that moment the sergeant-major who had by now lined his sights on the tinker, squeezed the trigger. At 75 yards the bullet went straight through the tinker's chest but in falling he still managed to throw the bundle at the barrack door where it lay on the step, spluttering. At the sound of the shot the piebald pony reared and neighed as two men jumped through the door of the caravan while another two slid from under the tarpaulin cover at the back. I could see that the front two were beardless boys wearing a sort of half uniform of leggings, bandoliers and soft hats with the side pinned up in the Australian fashion. The pony was now galloping down the street with the caravan lurching from side to side leaving the bleeding driver on the ground and the lethal bundle fizzing at the barrack door. From the barracks there was no sign of movement.

The two youths I could see were now hammering frantically on cabin doors to escape the unseen sniper but the sergeant-major, whose eyes were now wide and gleaming, had already worked the bolt of his rifle and lined up another target. As he squeezed the trigger there was a roar and a cloud of dust as the barrack door disintegrated with the explosion. It was only seconds later that I realised in my terror that the bedroom window lay in shards of glass around my shoulders and on the floor.

"Damn his eeyes ah had him deid,"

shouted McPherson as he shook the dust and glass from his helmet.

"Damn you, you butcher. Don't you think you have killed enough."

Now disgusted in my terror, I shouted this at the sergeant-major who looked at me bemused.

"Ah've sen twenty men killed by shellfire before breakfast time. Ah'm no a butcher ah'm a sodger. It's what ah'm pide tae dae."

When the dust had cleared the barrack door was gone, the spouting was hanging from the eaves and you could see the dun-painted corridor inside. Slates and masonry lay in the street. Most of the cabin windows had shattered too but no one ventured out. It was now nearly dark but the two IRA youths could still be seen running down the street. McPherson quickly worked the bolt of his rifle, fired and then shouted

"Got the bastard",

his eyes blazing. He again worked the bolt and took aim as the other youth stopped to help his companion. He fired and the other youth dropped over the body of his friend. The sergeant-major, now controlled and calm, sensed my outrage.

"We did'ny start this business in Ireland. Yon wee fuckers tried tae blow up my muckers in the barracks. They shouldn'y fecht it they canny dee."

The two other gunmen where nowhere to be seen in the dark but I imagine they had found refuge in the village. The police and soldiers now appeared on the street from the handball alley where they had been waiting. A Highland officer, incongruously waving what appeared to be a shepherds crook in one hand and a revolver in the other, ordered the soldiers to search the houses. Lights now appeared in the cabin windows as the villagers realised the attack was over and that they were safe from involvement.

The air was filled with shouts and curses as the soldiers set about their task with gusto, cracking the doors with their rifle butts if the owners failed to respond. I was frightened and sickened at the noise, the destruction and the bodies in the street and when McPherson thanked me for my co-operation and left the room I ignored him. I never saw him again and often wondered did he finish his service and settle into some mundane occupation such as a commissionaire where standing and watching without the fore knowledge of excitement was his lot. An air of sullen hostility pervaded the village, the resentment against the angry Scots increasing when it was realised that some gold sovereigns hidden under mattresses and in chimneys were missing. The barracks was declared unsafe and was abandoned, the small police detachment scattered round the county. Sergeant Crangle sent his family to stay with his wife's relatives in the North while he moved to Ennis, the county town. After his successful thwarting of the ambush he was a marked man and was offered a transfer to the North but he refused it on the grounds that his removal would be a victory for the shinners. He asked me to come and see him in Ennis which I did on occasion but he would never mention his daughter or the teacher Vesey.

"Without the law you have nothing",

he would say,

"and while I draw my pay for enforcing it, I will enforce it."

I gathered from these conversations that some of the police were turning a blind eye to the shinners knowing that they would be the power in the land when the British left, as they had already legislated for Home Rule in 1912.

The hotel became just another public house and the bridge games ceased. The farmers ceased to come to the fair days and their wives shopped in other villages.

Eventually the bank closed our branch, giving the manager and myself the opportunity of a transfer to the North which we readily accepted.

The village never really recovered as I found out when I passed through it some years ago. It was a desolate place bereft of youth and smelling of decay. America was now closed to emigration and the young men flocked to England where they earned high wages on the building sites. They would eventually marry and find it more convenient to live permanently in England so as the old people died the houses fell into crumbling ruins. In the main street a small statue of a nineteen twenties gunman had been erected. It was a miserable and squalid action that had been its inspiration. It was a five-foot figure of a man dressed in macintosh and leggings clutching a short barrelled rifle. His soft peaked cap was set back to front and he legend inscribed was "IN MEMORY OF VOLUNTEERS CONSIDINE, O'BRIEN AND SHEILDS, EAST CLARE BRIGADE OGLAIGH NA H'EIREANN, WHO SACRIFICED

THEIR LIVES FOR THEIR COUNTRY IN AN ATTACK AGAINST THE CROWN FORCES, MAY 1921.

The sculptor wisely witheld his name from his creation. Nobody remembered me there but one old lady had been friendly with the sergeant's wife and asked after his children. Five of the village girls had married Scots soldiers but seldom came home, probably due to living on army bases in the far flung empire of those days.

Because of my involuntary defence of the barracks at Kilkeshen I was moved to inform myself of the politics of Home Rule. It appeared to me that the whole bloody turmoil was unnecessary as it had already been granted for the south, and was being fiercely resisted in the north and that neither the British nor the insurgents had the power necessary to coerce them. I thought of the madness of men whose small value on human life caused the death of the young Scotsmen who are so like our own, the futility of the sacrifices of O'Brien, Considine, and Shields. I thought also of the dignity and principle of the stiff and unbending Sergeant Crangle, determined to uphold the law even to the extent of expelling his teenage daughter from the family.

For my own part I managed to progress in life in a slow orderly fashion that suited my retiring nature. I married a quiet colleague in the bank, our union being blessed with a son who is hard working in his chosen profession as a lawyer, also kind and thoughtful to his parents. I found that my work in the Bank Officials Union created a common purpose with my Protestant colleagues that made me feel, in my own insignificant way, that I would leave this life a little better than I found it.

Bridgeen Crangle leaned forward before I reached my stop and asked me would I have time for tea in her house before going home. I assured her I would be deeply honoured if I could telephone my son to collect me. We walked a few hundred yards from the tube stop to a Victorian terrace house which was the family home. Over tea she told me of her life which had not been easy. Michael Vesey had run off with her to Dublin where they had found a priest to marry them without the plethora of documents the church required at the time. He finished with the movement but the movement had not finished with him. He found out from a cousin that they were blaming him for the failure of the ambush in Kilkeshin as well they might.

"He did it for love of me and he knew how much I love my Dad,"
Bridgeen said quietly.

"We fled to London where Michael got a job teaching in a Catholic school and
we rented a church house where the three children were born. Miriam here is
in the Diplomatic Service in Brussels. My son is also a teacher here in London
and the eldest is in California married to an architect."

That she spoke in front of her children told me that this family had no secrets.

"Then Michael disappeared without note or call, just like that. At first I thought
that the shinners had got him at last, but Father Dempsey made discreet
enquiries and it was not so. That itself was a weight off my mind, but to this
day I don't know what made him go. At the time he had taken to drinking
with Scotchmen from the Islands in 'The Swan' on Harrow Road. He said
they spoke the Gaelic simply and naturally without making any statement and
you know he loved the language above all else. He often said they fared better
under the British than the Irish speakers did under their own. I thought he
might have gone to a teaching job in Harris or Skye but there was no trace of
him there either. We had rows but then who hadn't? I worked for the council
and I took in lodgers but it wasn't easy to rear four weans. The children
never visited their grandfather in Banbridge but knew their aunts and uncles
and the cousins, but hide nor hair have they ever seen of their da this thirty-
eight years."

Images of the rolling hills of Clare and the young Michael Vesey passed through
my head. It was a desperate course he had charted. Perhaps the wine of
young love had turned to vinegar in the unromantic reality of suburban London. Who knows, perhaps a Gaelic speaking sister of one of the Highlanders
he had tried to kill had captured his heart and again he had abandoned his
committments. That indeed would be the supreme irony. I was perplexed and
then angry. He had seemed to blight everything he touched. I made my fare-
wells promising to keep in touch as one does in these situations. I decided to
walk home to dwell on the picture that Bridgeen Crangle had painted, but
when I reached my son's house the story still left me with the same vexation
and frustration as a nearly completed crossword puzzle does. Bridgeen Crangle
had been a mere fifteen years old when she went away with Vesey, as yet an
unformed woman. Vesey had, as was common in Irish society of the time,
little knowledge or experience with love and sex. He had of course known

excitement and had shed blood but I thought that in a sense the pair of them were as young mongrel puppies whose temperament and appearance as fully grown dogs could not be forecast. All humankind changes and develops, influenced by society and by the close proximity of one's chosen life's partner, so perhaps for Michael Vesey the grown bitch was not the winsome beautiful puppy that had enthralled him.

Some weeks later back in the sombre wintry ambience of my retirement home and unable to sleep, I scanned the shortwave band of my receiver to home in on a symphony concert from Peking. The music was soothing and pleasant and was followed by a news broadcast delivered in a pronounced American accent. This was followed by a talk on linguistics as expounded by JV Stalin. The voice of the broadcaster astonished me into full attention. It was unmistakenly a full brogue from the west of Ireland. I was using a new Japanese receiver that my son had bought me which includes a facility for recording on tape. I had never used this before but I had a premonition that I would want to listen to this broadcast again. The very notion that an Irishman was expounding the teaching of Joe Stalin on Chinese radio was in itself bizarre. The broadcaster intoned:

"JV Stalin following the teaching of VI Lenin showed us that language is not a class category but a free standing means of communication shedding what is obsolescent and adding what is new and developing. Comrade Stalin wrote that language possesses great stability and a tremendous power of resistance to forcible assimilation. TheTurkish assimilators strove for hundreds of years to mutilate, shatter and destroy the language of the Balkan peoples. History shows us that as a result of mixture a language is enriched at the expense of a vanquished language. One is always the victor and one the vanquished. Russian always emerged the victor over the languages of the vanquished nationalities. In my own country Ireland the native Irish was vanquished by the stronger neighbour English and flourishes only in remote backward places and in the civil service, where it has become the passport to a sinecure for the national bourgeiose. Comrade Stalin, as commissar for nationalities under the great teacher Lenin, rescued many languages from extinction, gave alphabets where none existed and preserved them for historical and cultural studies. Irish on the other hand has become an archaic repository for names for folk groups and semi-state bodies."

The broadcaster continued:

"Under the leadership of the great helmsman Mao Tse Tung, following the teaching of Marx, Engels, Lenis and Stalin, we in the People's Republic of China revere the languages of the small nationalities and raise them to the pinnacle of cultural and linguistic attainment."

The broadcaster made his peroration with the following comment:

"Goodnight to all our English speaking listeners and to the Gaelgoiri of Ireland and Scotland, Oiche Mhaith."

I played the recording back and wondered if the broadcaster could have been Michael Vesey. The Scottish reference would be an indicator as Bridgeen Crangle had spoken of his interest in Scottish Gaelic. I decided to phone her the following evening.

When I telephoned Bridgeen I got the impresion that she felt uneasy speaking on the phone. I stated my purpose and she agreed to listen to the tape. Her voice assumed an edge sharpened by an almost impenetrable Clare accent.

"China is it? The right place for him, the huer's ghosht. Comrade Shtalion is it?"

She pronounced the Soviet leader's name as in a horse.

"I'll give him linguistics, the useless amadan. He would know more about mad dog shite than about linguistics, whatever they are, the bloody tinker's melt. Took me from my family when I was a slip of a girl and wouldn't go to Mass and cheeked the clergyman priest and got sacked, the little scut. God blasht the day I met him with his Eirinachs and his Albanachs and his Christ knows what achs, and now linguistics it it? Linguistics never put butter on my spuds." The tirade went on fluently for some time, halting only for Bridgeen to pause for breath.

I ventured to suggest that she should not upset herself, but take consolation that he was alive and well.

"Alive and well is it?"

she screamed down the phone,

"I'll give you alive and well. And what business of yours is it if he's alive and well. Bloody pen pushing counter hopper that sits down to pee! I'll thank you not to interfere with my family and get back to whatever bog you came from, you dirty dog with your filthy sexual practices."

The Patriarch

I decided that I had heard enough and quietly replaced the phone although I am fairly sure that this was not noticed and that the tirade would continue for some time.

There was a final word in the Daily Telegraph crossword puzzle that had eluded me all day. I lifted the paper and smiling to myself I pencilled it in.

The Leaving of Lvov

The blonde child rode her bike between the tramlines and the kerb avoiding the tramlines on one side and the rucks of snow on the other. Her head was covered in a fur hat with the earflaps tied down at the chin. A long single plait of blonde hair fell down from under her hat. Although fully formed at sixteen, Agniezka Jedrusek was still a child and as she rode her bike through the city of Lvov, formerly in Poland and now, in the winter of 1940, called Lviv in the Soviet Socialist Republic of Ukraine. The streetlamps shed an orange glow as the dusk gathered and the lights appeared in the dirty grey tenement blocks on either side of the road. The clanging of an approaching tramcar could be heard in the distance so Agniezka pedalled harder in order not to be hindered by the descending passengers at the tramstop. She pulled her kapok padded coat closer to her as the temperature was falling fast with the failing light. Her long nose, pale eyes and broad forehead showed her to be a Pole in this city of Poles, Ukrainians, Jews and other Slavic nationalities. The tramcar stopped behind her and disgorged its load of quilt-clad workers, male and female, who dispersed in different directions to their homes in the tenement blocks.

The crumbling grey tenements gave way to wooden houses with small gardens at front and rear and eventually Agniezka found herself past the tramcar terminal where the cobbled stone surface gave way to a metalled road. Some distance past the city boundary the orange streetlight system ended but ahead she could see the torches and lorry lights of a Red Army checkpoint. Agniezka was a courier for the A.K., the Armia Krajowa or Home Army, who were resisting the re-absorbtion of this part of former Poland into the Ukraine. The area has been ceeded to Poland in the Treaty of Brest Litvosk when the infant Soviet Union was on its knees and when Leon Trosky has been told to make peace with the victorious Poles, at any price. The price had been high with six million Ukrainians being handed over to Polish rule with most of the Western Ukraine. To Agnieska and the rest of her middle class family the loss of her native city to the Ukrainians was intolerable so her brother had left university for the dense forest lands where the Armia Krajova (Home Army) and hidden billets. Agniezka was on her way to this partisan unit with a message but ostensibly she was still a high school pupil. She experienced a frisson of fear as she approached the Red Army truck which was parked across the road requiring all traffic to halt while the Red Army peasant conscript boys lounged at its side, cigarettes in mouths. Their magnificent felt great coats reached nearly to the ground. They reminded Agniezka of the monks at a Catholic monastery she had visited but she knew they were there with the very purpose of frustrating the likes of herself. A young officer in a visored cap and leather map case stepped forward.

"Armia Czerwona! Proshe Pani dokumenty. Red Army! please madame your documents" he said politely. Agniezka proffered her passport telling him she was visiting her grandmother some miles out along the road. She spoke in Ukrainian which she knew the young officer, as a Russian, would understand giving the impression she was fully adjusted to the new political situation. The young officer saluted smartly, then waved her on as the conscripts smiled their approval, moving with elaborate gestures to clear way for her passage.

Agniezka cycled along the hard frozen road past the smallholdings with their low wooden houses to the edge of the forest. One of the six railway lines leading to Lvov hugged a deep ravine in the landscape and when she came to the bridge that crossed the line she turned off the road to a sandy track that lead into the forest. Her bicycle lamp showed the tracks of horses hooves in the sand causing Agniezka some worry lest the Red Army cavalry patrol had been past recently. A crust of ice had formed over the sand giving rise to a crunching sound as she walked. She was frightened of the dark trees which now met overhead blocking out the moonlight. To dispel her fears she self induced a warm glow of patriotism which surged through her as she summoned up the images of the red and white flag, the Polish Eagle insignia, also the map outline of the Polish state which had existed now for twenty years. Marshal Pilsudsky had carved out the frontiers of the modern Polish state had forced Trotsky, in Pilsudsky's eyes a Jewish Bolshevik, to concede the eastern provinces. Agniezka had the normal buds of awakening desire for love and sex but she subsumed these for the romatic love of country which surged in her breast. Her cascading blonde hair, regular features and shapely figure turned heads in her school and her home district but the earnest intensity of her demeanor repelled all dilletantes. In her youth she thought of Ladislas the Polish King who humbled the Teutonic knights at the battle of Tannenburg in 1412 and hoped that a man imbued with such a spirit would claim her for his bride.

The forests covered many thousands of hectares giving deep cover to the Colonel of reserves whose estates marched with it. Colonel Kot, code name "Jurek" had not surrendered to the Red Army but asked for volunteers to follow him into its depths. A lamp flashing dot dash, dash dot dash, awakened Agniezka from her reverie and dispelled her anxiety. This was the morse for A.K. signifying that her brother Tadeusz was waiting. He was tall and blond like herself and wore an army lieutenant's uniform. Five years older than Agniezka, Tadeusz had been an architect and a reserve officer. Although he did not like his colonel's imperious aristocratic ways he was appalled at the idea of spending the war in a P.O.W. camp deep in Kazakistan or some such place without a shot being fired. He embraced his sister, enquired after their parents who continued to teach in Polish schools and then asked for the message which he would commit to paper. The message was simple and was committed to memory by Agniezka

"The city soviet meets at the townhall in the market square in the old town at 3.30 on Friday. By the way 'Josef's soldiers' were on the road but I told them I was visiting my grandmother along the road. Our parents send their love and pray for you. Mother also has told the district committee that you were taken prisoner by the Germans at Warsaw."

Agniezka reached up and pulled her brother's lean bony face to her own, hugged him and then watched him as he retreated into the vastness of the forest.

The inaugural meeting of the City Soviet for Lvov district was chaired by Wladislaw Gomulka and consisted of delegates from all the district committees. For the most part they were Polish but there were Ukrainians and Jews there as well. There were also delegates from the railway stations and factory works councils. All in all about a hundred delegates sat in the old town hall in the market square. The hall was decorated by Soviet, Ukrainian and Polish flags behind the platform, with a large portrait of Marshal Stalin on the back wall. The bust of Lenin on the podium seemed small by comparison.

Gomulka welcomed the delegates to the meeting which he said would be conducted in the Polish language with simultanious translation into Ukrainian and Yiddish. Wladislaw Gomulka was a small middle-aged man with a larged domed prematurely bald head who had been imprisoned for his trade union activity in the Polish military dictatorship. He was the leader of the chemical workers union and had also been in the first rank of the Polish Communist Party which was dissolved by the International on the grounds of heavy infiltration by government agents. He was a practised orator, respected and admired by his audience. They were mostly workers with lined faces and gnarled hands, old before their time with constant toil in the smokey railway workshops and antiquated factories of Lvov. Their clothes were their best serge and every man had made an effort to appear in a clean collar and tie. Here and there were groups of women in headscarves and shawls, anxious about their prisoner-of-war husbands and sons. The university was represented by a bank of soft skinned men and women whose well groomed appearance was in stark contrast to that of the workers. Gomulka explained the necessity of the Soviet-German pact due to refusal of the western allies to sign a defensive pact to save Czechoslovakia with the help of the Soviet Union. The Red Army had occupied the Western Ukraine and Vilno to halt the German advance. The deliniation of the new frontier would take place after the Germans were expelled from Czechoslovakia and our beloved Poland. Our own military dictatorship had seized lands occupied by the Czechs when Hitlerites invaded that country. The Western Allies had not the will to defend Czechoslovakia and Poland and their phoney war in France has taught us that only the army of the working class, the Armia Czerwona, can defend the interests of the working class. Gomulka's voice rose with passion as he delivered this sentence. His oratory resonated within the audience who rose and cheered to the emotional appeal to working class solidarity.

He continued his speech accompanying each policy statement with a slicing motion of his right arm.

"All nationalities were guaranteed full civic rights and were encouraged to take part in building socialism. Free health services, free education and rights to pensions at fifty-five for those doing heavy manual work would be implemented as in the Soviet Union. Jewish, Ruthenian, German, Armenian and other minority groups would have full civic rights. All large enterprises would be taken into public ownership. Schools previously controlled by the Catholic church would be taken over by the City Soviet and those clerics who show a progressive attitude will be kept on as teachers. Those who preach sectarian and hostile attitudes to the international proletariat must earn their living by the sweat of their brows, as we do, comrades!"

The delegates who were mostly from the left wing groupings of the three main nationalities again rose to their feet and cheered. Wladislaw Gomulka continued his address saying that there were right-wing nationalist forces in the city who would try to sabotage this programme but that they would be dealt with fearlessly by the Red Army and the security forces. The delegates clapped hard at this statement.

The elections of the various committees of the City Soviet followed and the meeting finished with the singing of the "Internationale" in the three languages.

It was dark now, the yellow street lamps shining on the muddied snow on the footpath. A clanking tramcar lurched its way down the nearly deserted square, its passengers huddled against the cold. Everyone about sought the heat and comfort of home except the three Soviet policemen opposite the entrance of the townhall. They stamped their feet, engaging in desultory conversation as men whose function it is to watch and wait often do. A small Citroen car parked across the road from the meeting place awaited Comrade Gomulka. The driver sat as if asleep but in fact he was dead, shot through the heart by a silenced revolver. The meeting over, the delegates streamed out through the hallway to the square where some stood in knots continuing the discussion or exchanging pleasantries. Mostly the delegates dispersed in different directions through the side streets. A group of Jewish garment workers continued an animated discussion on the pavement for some time after the others had dispersed. Then Wladislaw Gomulka appeared in the hallway with his bodyguard. This was the signal for the attack. The three policemen on the other side of the street drew their revolvers, emptying the chambers into the group outside the hallway. Three of the Jewish workmen fell mortally wounded. A fourth, an elderly tailor, his large brown eyes wide with fear and pain, blood darkening his old fashioned high buttoned coat, crawled inside the hallway moaning the age old warning

"Pogrommy! Progrommy!"

The survivors of the attack pulled the old man into the hallway where life departed from his body. Gomulka's bodyguard had rushed upstairs in time to see the assassins running from the scene. Opening the landing window, he crouched on one knee and fired once. One of the assassins fell while another stopped to lift him. The bodyguard took careful aim and fired again. The bending figure also fell while the third assassin cleared the corner and disappeared into the warren of small cobbled streets off the market square. One of the assassins was dead and the other mortally wounded when the ambulance arrived to clear the charnal house outside the city hall. Before he died, the wounded Home Army soldier, not wanting to betray his safe house in the city, told the N.K.V.D. officer that had come from the forest. The survivor made his way to the appartment of Aghiezka Jedrusek's parents. This man was a tough regular Polish Army sergeant of early middle age who had come through the '39 campaign, a man who had seen much bloodshed, a coarse-grained man who obeyed orders without question, who would meet death halfway with a smile on his face. He was a Silesian from Katowice who was now technically a German citizen and would have been forced into Hitler's Wehrmacht had he returned to what was now a German province. Being thoroughly institutionalised and unable to cope with life outside a uniform he elected to follow Colonel Kot, now "Jurek", into the forest. As he was unfamiliar with the city the Jedruseks had to devise a way to smuggle him out of Lvov, which they did by dressing him in Agniezka's old coat and a headscarf which hid his face. A pair of knee high leather boots hid his legs. His coarse skin was smoothed with layers of powder. The disguise was effective enough to bring Agniezka, posing as his daughter, and himself to the end of the tramcar lines without arousing any interest. The walk out to the end of the forest proved uneventful. No Red Army road block was encountered so Agniezka was able to take back her mother's identity document. Agniezka's feelings towards her companion were mixed. The man was rough spoken and insensitive and yet he was a hero of the underground who had carried out a successful mission. He showed no grief for his wounded and dead comrades and did not know or seem to care who he killed. To her the victims of the ambush were unprincipled collaborators and Jewish communists who had betrayed their country. It annoyed her when her companion, with apparent relish, had described the charnal house he had left on the market square. Her brother was waiting at the same spot on the forest track, to be greeted by a smart military salute from the sergeant still dressed in his woman's clothes.

For the first time in many months she gave voice to gales of laughter soon joined by her brother. The dour sergeant muttered an obscenity, tearing off the woman's clothes as he did so.

While Aniezka reached her parents' apartment the Interior Ministry troops were already there. A middle-aged officer with a thin dark visage asked her (in Yiddish accented Polish) if she was Agniezka Jedrusek.

"There is no need to lie to me. I know you are a courier for the right-wing bandits in the forest. We followed you there and have arrested Kot's gang, your brother amongst them. Unfortunately they were all Polish army soldiers wearing uniforms of sorts so they will be treated as prisoners of war. The atrocity on the market square killed four decent workers and wounded many more. These were men and women who devoted their lives to bettering the lot of their fellow man, the cream of the proletariat of Lvov cut down by murderous right-wing gangsters. One of them was my own brother, a veteran of the International Brigade."

His voice rose with emotion.

"To think of a man who survived Franco's fascist beasts to die such a squalid death at the hands of a fellow Pole. Now you must tell me who was the bastard dressed as a woman you brought to the forest. We know he was the third assassin."

Agniezka was shaking with fear. She was a Polish patriot yet she did not feel she should lay down her life for the unlettered oaf who walked with her to the forest. She must be brave she thought and not answer anything.

"I am a soldier in the Armia Krajowa and according to the Geneva convention I am only required to give you my name, rank and number."

"You are a stupid silly girl who will be tried by military tribunal for assistance to murder and if you are not executed you will be locked up with thieves and prostitues for the rest of your life",

shouted the officer.

Agniezka, knowing the penalties for working for the underground, composed herself and, feeling the nationalist fervour rising within her, stared straight at the officer without blinking.

"Your brother was not a Pole, surely he was Jewish",

responded Agniezka who was genuinely curious about this man who was in a Soviet uniform and spoke fluent Polish. She was no anti-Semite and had gone to high school with Jewish girls but always considered them separate and different. Because they spoke Yiddish amongst themselves and kept to themselves she had never considered them to be Polish. The Ukrainians she could understand because they resented being in Poland and were wishful to be part of another country, but what were the Jews who had been part of Polish life for hundreds of years. Her parents, as professional people resented the Jews as competitors and she often heard them say "They would sell us if they could", and wondered what they meant. The officer's lip tightened as he drew in breath, his dark eyes narrowed with pain and anger and he made an effort to control his temper.

"My brother was a Polish citizen of Jewish origin and I am a Soviet citizen of Jewish nationality. You try and be Polish and a human being! Pani Jedrusek the day is over when a Jew can be shot like a rabbit or insulted in the street. I ask you once again who was the disguise artist who dressed up as a policeman and then as a woman? I will keep asking the question until I get an answer."

After four hours the guards had fallen asleep on her mother's couch but the officer was still asking Agniezka the same question. Eventually she remembered her brother telling her when he went in the army how difficult it was to train the Ukrainan conscripts who spoke no Polish and who hated being in the army in the first place. Feigning a complete breakdown Agniezka wept as she told the officer how the third man wass an unlettered Ukrainian peasant conscript, with whom she could have no understanding, who probably had deserted or joined up with Stepan Bandera's Ukrainian nationalist bandits who were also operating in the forest. The officer seemed to accept this as Agniezka was led away from her weeping parents to the Lvov's women's prison.

Agniezka's spirits rose as she was escorted in the prison van to the prison. She had outwitted the N.K.V.D. officer and had probably saved the Polish army sergeant from the firing squad. She was, she felt, a heroine of Poland and would be recognised as such when the French and British armies swept across Europe and liberated her homeland. However when the van entered the grim stone prison building, Agniezka's confidence evaporated to be replaced by a deep despair.

Built by the Czars to encarcerate the female criminals and revolutionaries of Lvov and district, it exuded of the human spirit. She was led to the colonel's office for the formal induction procedure and to her surprise she found herself in the presence of middle-aged Polish women wearing military uniform with colonel's epaulettes. She introduced herself as Colonel Halina Bednarska, a former prisoner in the prison, as a Communist in the time of the Polish military dictatorship. She explained that like Agniezka she was a political prisoner but unlike her she had committed no crime. It was enough to have been in the Communist party. She told Agniezka she had behaved in a very wicked way letting herself be a tool of the catholic nationalist bourgeoisie but nevertheless she would be well treated until her courtmartial. Halina Bednarska had been a textile worker in Lodz, rebelled against the long hours and harsh conditions by joining the textile workers union and eventually became a full-time organiser and a party member. When a greedy factory owner introduced a speedup the girls voted to strike. Halina organised the pickets and the other factories came out in sympathy. The Polish dictator had her and the strike committee arrested and then the strike collapsed. When the others were released Halina was interned and spent most of her time in this prison. The arrival of the Red Army emptied the prison and as Halina knew the prison regime they asked her to run it. Her face was lined beyond her years, her hair was prematurely white but her sky blue eyes, which showed much suffering, were kind. She told Agniezka to show some compassion for her fellow Poles who were destitute and hungry in peace as well as in war. She quoted the Irish communist James Connolly who had said, "Ireland without her people is nothing."

"The ally of the Polish working class is the Soviet Union and it's enemy is German fascism",

Colonel Bednarska continued. Agniezka instinctively warmed to this motherly woman but understood nothing of politics. For Agniezka it was simple. The Germans had invaded and smashed the Polish army and the Russians had taken the other half of her country.

The prison cell was built for one prisoner but now held three and as the door clanged shut Agniezka's courage deserted her. She was thrown into a paroxism of despair, her body racked with shuddering sobs. The cell was all stone and metal apart from the deal table and three-tier bunk bed. One of the occupants was a Gipsy girl also in her teenage years while the other was a middle-aged blousy blonde prostitute who spoke only German. The German woman had a bosom ballooning out of her grey prison shift, her blue-grey eyes seemed dead, like a fish's, lying in a face of yellow putty surrounded by grey-blonde curls. She was there for separating a client from his wallet. She put her arm round Agniezka mouthing soothing incomprehensible words.

"Ach du kliene Kindeskopf allien in dieses smutzige Gefangnis in Lemburg."

"Little childhead all alone in this dirty jail in Lvov."

Agniezka only recognised the German word for Lvov.

"Lemberg" was often used by her grandparents who grew up as citizens of the Austro-Hungarian Empire and she was grateful for this identification with her native city. The Gipsy girl vacated the bottom bunk and nimbly sprinted to the top one leaving the prostitute to the middle. Agniezka composed herself by self induction of the nationalist spirit that was deep in her psyche. Emotionally exhausted she fell asleep, but her dreams became erotic, forming images in her head she would not have wished. She dreamt she was on holiday in the Carpathian mountains to the south of the city with the peasant's son who used to help her father around his holiday cottage. He was kissing her neck. He was moving his groin against her buttocks, his fingers lightly tracing the fronds of her pudenda. His thrusts became harder and swifter while his fingers were roughly exploring the lips of her purse. Agniezka screamed as she wakened to find the prostitute behind her in the bunk kissing her neck and thrusting her bare body against her's. Agniezka tore the probing hands away, pulling herself out of the bunk to scream abuse at the woman and then to pummel her with her fists. The Gipsy girl, brown and agile as a cat, slid down from the top bunk, joining in the fracas. They both punched and kicked the German woman, her cries of "Hilfe" unheeded in the darkness of the jail. The Gipsy girl related how she too had been assaulted in the dark by the prostitute who was obviously only interested in men for money. This common unpleasant experience established a bond between the two girls that helped Agniezka come to terms with her situation. She thought of the contempt she had for Gipsies before and now here she was, a well-born Polish student, comrade to a Gypsy thief in a Ukrainian prison. Agniezka's trial was perfunctory; A soviet policeman related how he had watched the Jedrusek apartment and followed her to the forest with a man disguised as a woman which led the security forces to the nationalist camp where the Colonel known as Jurek was captured with his men. They believed that the third assasin was a Ukrainian now with the Ukrainian right-wing bandits. Because Agniezka was under eighteen she was spared the death penalty for assisting in a murder and was sentenced to five years in a labour camp category 3 with light labour, in Siberia.

The army lorry that bore Agniezka from the prison turned down Ackademicka Street with its fine houses and shops into Pl. Mickiewicz with it's statue of the national poet, up Kopernicus Street which honoured the Polish astronomer who discovered the solar system, to the Lvov railway station. Agniezka cried softly to herself as she wondered when she would ever see her native city again. The Gipsy girl and she stayed together fearful of preditory advances by the other prisoners but they seemed to be mostly politicals with a few convicted speculators. The politicals distanced themselves from Agniezka because of her friendship with the Gipsy girl. They all seemed to be upper class women whose husbands had been highly placed in the prewar Polish police, military and civil service. They regarded the Russians and Ukrainians as barbarians and as for Gipsies it was the ultimate degradation to be forced to be in their close company.

The railway station was crowded with military lorries packed with prisoners and guarded by military policemen with automatic rifles at the ready. As each lorry approached the station the prisoners would dismount, form up in fours and, circled by military policemen, be marched to the station platform where the longest train Agniezka had ever seen awaited. The prisoners were then lined up outside a carriage door where an officer checked their names off a clipboard after which they filed aboard a carriage whose windows were barred. As the lorries drew up to the platform Agniezka scanned the ranks of prisoners for her brother and sure enough a lorry filled with officers in smart zigzag braided uniforms lined up to be embarked. They had obviously made an effort to express a parade ground demeanour, responding to the commands of "Jurek", their aristocratic colonel. Agniezka spotted her brother in the front row and leaning half way out of the lorry shouted

"Tadeusz, Tadeusz! it's Agniezka".

Her brother looked over and overjoyed at seeing his sister, jumped up and down waving his arms crying out family endearments. The granite-faced Colonel Kot, aloof and unbending, bellowed a call to attention.

"Lieutenant Jedrusek! How dare you break discipline! You are a Polish officer. Behave like one".

The Russian officer with the clipboard smiled to himself as he counted the line into the barred carriage. Tadeusz resented his commanders's lack of humanity.

The barred carriage proved to be an ordinary passenger carriage with a section at the end containing bunks for the guards, a samovar and an oil stove. There were ordinary passenger seats, but not enough room for the two hundred women some of whom were forced to sit on their bags. Some of the women were cursing their husbands whose ill treatment of communists, socialists and Jewish bundists had put them in this position. Others wept silently while the criminals whose had seen the inside of many jails accepted their lot philosophically. Agniezka drew comfort from the brief greeting from her brother and took pleasure in snubbing the rich women who now acknowledged her as the brother of a Polish officer. The military police officer again checked the name against his list. The train and it's miserable cargo pulled out of the station bound for Irkutsk.

Meals were very basic; black tea and black bread for breakfast and lunch. Evening meal was a cabbage soup with perhaps an ounce of meat in it if one were lucky. Some of the middle-class women had tried to bribe the young conscript military policemen with jewels in order to obtain better fare but they explained that there was only the makings of the soup on the train and they had to make do with the same diet. The flat Ukrainian steppe with its unending blanket of snow yielded no visual interest but sometimes the train slowly negotiated crowded railway junctions where there were the longest feight trains the Poles had ever seen. Some of them were a mile long, being drawn by several engines. It was rumoured that Stalin was sending entire factories beyond the Urals complete with their workers. The Romany girl could speak Russian as well as Ukrainian, German, Slovakian and Polish, having travelled with her nomad family as a child. Agniezka was fascinated with this ability, having formerly regarded Gipsies as illiterate criminals. The Gipsy girl, whose name was Anna, explained to her that they had their own Romany language which they used among themselves. She had been imprisoned on the foot of a fortune-telling scam which involved the handing over of silver rings which, they had assured the Ukrainian peasants, would be turned into gold by a magic fluid. The silver rings found their way into the Gipsy's pocket and the gold rings turned green after a few hours. Agniezka had to laugh at Anna's audacity.

The train passed through Kiev and then Moscow marshalling yards, where they saw again huge trains, some loaded with machinery and some packed with people. The military guards were changed, more cabbages and potatoes loaded but, try as they would, the prisoners could not venture through the train or stretch their legs in the snow. Anna had enquired about the Polish officers from the young flat-faced Siberian soldier. He told them that they had to lie on the floor on hay as did the soldiers and complained bitterly, citing the Geneva convention. The Siberian said that they treated the guards like servants and had referred to himself as an Asiatic barbarian. The Siberian feared there would be trouble with the Polish officers before the journey was over but agreed to take a greeting from Agniezka to her brother. Leaving Moscow, the forested landscape closed the train with a wall of darkness. Agniezka felt sweaty and dirty and being a city girl she yearned for the sight of human habitation. As water was scarce the guards would scoop up the snow from the sidings when they got a chance and on the whole behaved as decently as the circumstances allowed. Then thirty hours out from Moscow some of the women became ill from influenza and the virus quickly infected half of the women. Agniezka and Anna organised a standing rota so that the most affected got a chance to lie down. By this time all social barriers had broken down, criminals bathed the brows of sickened upper class ladies and wives of estate owners emptied the shit pans of former prostitutes. There was no medical officer on board but the train commander telegraphed ahead to a halt in the Ural mountains for medicines. An army doctor came on board, took some temperatures but refused to allow any one off the train. He left a bag of aspirins for relief of pain. The train commander told the women there was no hospital within a hundred miles so they were better off in the warmth of the train. Because of the epidemic food was more plentiful, giving the ones who had succumbed a chance to build up their strength. Agniezka began to find her spirits rising with the return of a more purposeful existence as a nurse. She had also learned some tricks of survival from Anna whose whole life had been a struggle against society. Some of the high officials' wives still affected an air of superiority and treated with disdain those they regarded as being of lower orders.

As the train wound its way down the mountain passes onto the Siberian tundra two women with heart conditions died. Lack of comfort and the ravages of the virus had done for them and their deaths excised any positive resurgence with Agniezka. The guards wrapped the corpses in blankets and carried them through the train to the baggage carriage where the minus 30 temperature would preserve them.

Eventually the train reached the Siberian city of Irkutsk. The prisoners, however, did not see much of the city or of the famous Lake Baikal nearby. A fleet of lorries waited by the station. Ringed by guards, two thousand prisoners were loaded into the lorries, shivering in the Arctic temperatures, awaiting they knew not what. The lorries crawled through the deserted city, the sound of the snow chains crushing the ice drowning the quiet sobs of the women. Agniezka reflected how much her life had changed and how her values had altered since she entered Lvov prison. She had aged five years in five weeks but now felt quite confident and able to face whatever hardships, moral or physical, that life could bring. She gathered her quilted jacket round her, stretched her aching legs and did something she had never done before. She threw back her head and sang the Polish anthem 'POLAND WILL NEVER DIE'. Everybody learned it at school and knew snatches of the song so it wasn't long until all the women were singing. The prisoners in the other lorries took up the refrain, even the guards who seemed to know the tune. Agniezka again surprised herself at her ability to show leadership when it seemed to be necessary.

The convoy slowly proceeded up into the low hills above Irkutsk sometimes halted by a truck slewing across the ice. This would force the guards and prisoners to climb down and haul the vehicle out of the ditch. There was no effort to escape as a deep inpenetrable bush known as the taiga surrounded the road. It was also heavily wooded with birch and pine, metres deep in snow and apparently uninhabited. The Gypsy girl Anna asked the guards to tell them about their destination but these were mostly fresh-faced farm boys who had just finished their recruit training at the Interior Ministry troop depot. Four hours later a glow of yellow halogen light appeared on the horizon. It was indeed the prison camp which was to be their home. Everybody,

guards, officers and prisoners, were glad to see what promised to be a res-
pite from the cold and misery of the truck convoy. The camp was newly built
and consisted of hundreds of wooden buildings squared by a ten-foot-high
wooden palisade fence with an illuminated watchtower at each corner. A
barrack square in the middle of the camp was the off-loading point for the
trucks. The registration procedures were carried out quickly and efficiently.
Everyone co-operated in order to get out of the freezing Siberian night air.
The prisoners lined up a draw their bedding, eating utensils, felt boots and
gloves, in a huge reception hall beside the stores. All Agniezka's mind could
register was sleep and warmth.

Four hours later the forty women in her hut were wakened and told to proceed to the washroom. They washed in relays of twenty, all modesty gone,
the women showered with relish for the first time in a week. Four of the
women were still ill with influenza that had spread through the train. Anna
had asked the guard to call a doctor and indeed a Russian woman doctor was
attending them when they returned. Her white gown and mask over the Kapok jacket and pants looked incongruous but she seemed competent. Her
diagnosis was grim. Pneumonia, it seemed, had developed due to exposure to
the Siberian night while still weak with influenza. They were to stay in bed
and their comrades were to feed them gruel and aspirins morning and night.
The two guards assigned to their hut were Russian and Armenian. Both were
anxious to please their charges but both were aware of the penalties for
breaking the rules. Georgi, the Russian one, called out for the women to
stand by their beds, an order which was quickly interpreted by Anna. The
camp commander arrived with his entourage. He was a fat low-set Russian
with beetle brows and a blunt peasant's face. It was obvious that he revelled
in his authority. He doffed his Astrakhan cap to reveal shining black hair
brushed flat back from the front. The belt on his greatcoat was fastened at
the last button. He surveyed the woman with his small dark eyes. One could
see that he liked what he saw. He gave a pompous cough in preparation for
his address.

"Prisoners! You have arrived at Labour Brigade Dzerzhinsky where you will
serve your sentences. You have as youy see new quarters and you will work
at various enterprises which we have undertaken. You will be paid three
roubles a week out of which your board and lodging will be deducted. You

will also pay for the board and lodging of those who cannot for various reasons work, such as age or infirmity. As the enterprises are self-sufficient you must also pay for the maintenance of the camp and the costs of security. In the camp you will find civilian workers who have volunteered to set up the stitching factory and the logging enterprise. These skilled workers will teach you your jobs. They are all patriotic Soviet citizens who volunteered to help fullfil the five-year plans of the various industries. Any attempt to corrupt or subvert them will be dealt with harshly. You will work from seven a.m. till two p.m. and from two p.m. you will attend lectures and discussion on Marxism-Leninism, history and literature. Those of you who are illiterate will be taught literacy. It is our duty to reform and rehabilitate you and be useful citizens of the Soviet Motherland. You will now have your heads shaved for purpose of hygiene".

The commander delivered this oration without expression or emotion but his black pig's eyes lit up when he told them of the requirement to have shaven heads. The middle-class women were horrified but the few criminals told them it was better to have a bald skull than headlice which were common in jails. The barber, a Polish P.O.W., duly arrived to cut the hair giving Agniezka the chance to enquire about her brother. He was fit, the soldier told her, but there was trouble at the officers compound as Colonel Kot had informed the commander that his officers would refuse to work, as was their right according to the Geneva convention. The commander had replied that the other ranks would have the cost of the officers' board and keep deducted from their pay. Colonel Kot had also refused to have two Jewish reserve officers in his hut. The Jewish officers, an architect and a surveyor, immediately volunteered to work at their professions in the building of the camp extension and were allowed the privileges of civilian workers. The policemen's wives were delighted that the Colonel stood up to the commander until they realised that they would get no pay. They then cursed him.

In the Polish officers' compound a thousand officers maintained military protocol, saluting each other when they met, calling all higher ranks "sir" and so forth. Those who were pragmatic about their situation realised that the refusal to work would cause hardships for their men and indeed be counter-productive, as sitting around idle in cold huts would undermine the officers' morale. Tadeusz, Agniezka's brother, was horrified at the regular officers' contempt for Russians, Ukrainians and Jews. Tadeusz was beginning to real-ise that the military dictatorship had cultivated an ethos of grandiose military elitism which was probably responsible for the debacle of the Polish army in its defence of Warsaw. Most of the regular officers were excellent horsemen who ignored the new mechanized warfare and led cavalry charges against the panzers. Tadeusz began to realise that these men did not even acknowledge their culpability but revelled in the nobility of their defeat. Colonel Kot's distainful attitude to the guards resulted in them getting cold tea and soup, later delivery of wood for the fire, and the other petty punishments. The final straw was the expulsion of the Jewish officers from the hut. To Tadeusz, as for most Poles, the national honour was embodied in the Polish army and those who wore its uniform were worthy of respect regardless of religion or national origin, Tadeusz was beginning to harbour feelings of emnity towards the military caste. He confided his feelings to one or two of the other reservists who agreed but advocated caution as these militarists were all-powerful, even in the prison camp.

Agniezka had never worked a sewing machine before; her fingers were all thumbs, causing the Russian instructress to curse under her breath. There were five hundred machines, made in Kharkov, all humming inside two huge wooden sheds. Piles of brown serge cloth lay heaped round the walls. Even-tually Agniezka got the hang of sewing up the seams of trousers for the Red Army. She even got to like the work, taking a pride in the accuracy of her stitches. The noise of five hundred whirring machines was irritating but she soon got used to it, judging the finishing of a row of stitches in time with her neighbour so that she could shout a comment. A young Polish P.O.W. from the Tatra mountains pushed a trolly between the lines of machines collecting the finished garments. He said he was lucky to get an indoor job instead of marching to the timber stands in the cold to toil all day with horses and saws. He was a well-built youth with sad dreamy eyes and lank brown hair that kept falling over his eyes when he lifted the finished garments. His parents lived on an acre on the mountainside and he told Agniezka his nine brothers and sisters often went hungry when his father had no work. His meagre army pay of a few zloties was the first steady money the family had known. Henryk had served on the Soviet frontier with the Carpathian Brigade who were sur-rounded in the first hour of the invasion. They had come straight to Irkutsk, sleeping in the trucks until the first hut was built. Now that the camp was finished, conditions were much better even if the food was lacking in nutrients. He had been attending the literacy classes after work but then "Jurek" had forbidden them to co-operate with the Russians. Also the fact that the officers refused to work meant they never had any money for the canteen for razor blades or soap. He was however friendly with the guards when there were no Polish officers about and he was fast learning Russian as many of the words were the same. He also got pieces of the odd snow rabbit that they trapped. Henryk felt as though Agniezka was a sister, completely trustworthy, clever and beautiful. Agniezka felt waves of pity for this angelic boy, poor and uneducated, caught up in something he could not comprehend.

From time to time the commandant would make his rounds of the factory, stopping here and there to question the prisoners. The women always complained about the poor diet but he would counter with his gold-toothed smile and blame the warehouses in Irkutsk for cutting the rations. To the more attractive women he would suggest they commit their complaints to paper and present them to him in his office in the afternoon. The women knew what he had in mind but a few took up his offer and returned reeking of vodka. It soon became clear extra food could also be bought from the commander with jewels and dollars. Henryk told Agniezka that the commander also sold stores to the Siberian hunters who lived in the forest. Agniezka noted the dates and times of the commander's trysts while Henryk supplied her with the dates and times he knew the Siberians had collected stores.

The human mind adapts to the routine and limitations of existence; a little high point of life would be a leg of rabbit from Henryk or a dog eared book in Polish that somebody had brought. The steady routine of work, sleep, recreation and sleep however was disrupted when word came down from the officers' huts that the women were to sabotage production of the uniforms. They had heard that the Germans and British were fighting side by side against the Soviet Union on the Finnish front and that the Germans might ally themselves with the western allies to overthrow the Soviet Union. In that case the British would prevail upon Hitler to withdraw from Poland with some territorial concessions. The camp lectures told a different story of how the imperialists were uniting to overthrow the first workers' state and that it was in the interest of all the workers to defend socialism and democracy everywhere.

Finland was a military dictatorship which had taken advantage of the weakness of the early Soviet state as had Pilsudsky in Poland. Agniezka worried about the difficulties disruption of production would cause in the congenial working environment but felt it was her duty as a soldier in the Armia Czerwona to implement orders. She decided to confide in Anna whom she regarded as a loyal friend. Anna's instinctive response was to advise her friend to ignore the officers' orders, disassociate herself from their ridiculous army and get herself released as soon as possible.

"Dear Agniezka, I am here for tricking stupid peasants. I have no such option, but you have. Anyway if you organize something the Commander will soon know about it from the women who sell themselves for food and vodka".

Agniezka decided to put it to a meeting after evening meal which was served in the hut. The "szlachta" or landed gentry, as Agniezka had designated the middle class women, used the occasion to vent their spleen on the "Asiatic savages" who guarded them but shied away from any action that would bring retribution to their heads.

"In that case we will forget about the whole idea and confine ourselves to agitating for more food".

Agniezka, having misled the other women in the hut, devised a plan whereby she could carry out sabotage without anybody, not least the other prisoners, being aware of it.

She had noticed that the finished trousers were folded up with only a cursory examination before packed in bales for transportation. Nobody, it seemed, examined the separate trouser legs. She decided to sew the two legs together which she could easily do now that she was an accomplished stitcher. Henryk was instructed to convey to the officers that sabotage in the stitching room was being effected. Henryk told her of beatings being administered in the P.O.W. huts by N.C.O.'s on the instructions of "Jurek". A certain regular army sergeant was reporting everything back to Colonel Kot. The orders to sabotage the logging had caused great difficulties for the men. When the tractors were damaged it meant that the men had to stand around in the freezing Siberian winter while they were repaired. If the machinery was out of action for long the men had to drag the logs manually to the stacking bays. This was a severe tax on already undernourished men. There had been a fatal accident when a log had been dropped on a soldier's leg. The soldier was buried outside the camp beside the two women who had succumbed to pneumonia. The sabotage campaign also generated hostility from the guards who in turn would be punished for lack of vigilance. This meant that the sub rosa gifts of taiga rabbits ceased. Agniezka knew from Henryk's description of the sergeant informer that this was the same man that she had smuggled out of Lvov after the assassinations. All of this made her very uneasy in her loyalties which were very dear to her as a Polish nationalist. She lay in bed at night considering her life. Instead of being an esteemed patriot in the eyes of her compatriots in the hut her only friend was a wandering Gipsy who claimed no nationality and her only other confidant was a poor mountain lead whose life had been an unequal struggle against hunger and poverty. Henryk's only salvation, were it not for the war, would have been emigration. As so often happens in life, the others noticed her increasing attachment to Henryk before she realised this herself. Anna ribbed her about it but she reassured herself more than Anna that her only emotion was an overwhelming compassion.

Anna for her part had realised, coming from a long line of survivers, that she somehow had to win acceptance from the szlachta who had a significant amount of jewellery about their persons. She did this by teaching a former wardress the rudiments of a fashionable card game. Gradually, through boredom, the other drifted over to watch and eventually they asked to be included in the game. Anna had a small stock of gold rings, one of which she offered as a wager. Soon the other women were staking their wedding rings on the cards. After losing steadily for a while Anna, through shameless cheating, relieved them of most of their jewellery. She also earned a few kopecks every day from the guards whose tea cups she read. She never played cards again or initiated any social contact with the aristocrats. In the officers' prison compound, Tadeusz Jedrusek was becoming more and more disillusioned with the fascist and militarist attitudes of "Jurek" and his coterie of regular army majors. They seemed to ignore the annexation of Poland proper by the Nazis to marshall all their hatred and resentment at the Soviet Union.

"Pilsudski should have pressed on to Moscow and extirpated the Bolshevik swine"

was a typical remark that was passed. They seemed to have contempt for the men they led whose only function it would appear was to fight and die for the honour of Poland. Tadeusz, who had an ear for languages, was picking up Russian with ease and was working his way through the classics - Chekov, Tolstoy, Gorky - and the new writers Mayakovsky and Ehrenberg. He and a few of the other reserve officers had formed a choir whose repertoire was mainly Polish folksongs. This was not encouraged by the regulars who dismissed the folksongs as "peasant" music. One reservist, who spoke English, taught them the air and words of a Scottish folksong 'Loch Lomond' which later became a favourite with Polish choirs everywhere.

Springtime came late to Siberia but when it came it was an awe inspiring reaffirmation of life. The snow melted, the rivers burst into life and a thousand different forest flowers pushed through the newly thawed earth. Agniezka received several letters from her family who carried on with their life in Lvov and carefully advised her to keep to the rules and pray for a quick release. On June 22 1941 Hitler's panzers crossed the Soviet border, surrounding hundreds of thousands of Red Army infantry and artillery, then sweeping through the Ukraine, Lithuania and White Russia. Lvov, Pinsk and Vilnius were overrun in a few days. The Colonels and Majors seemed pleased but the attitude of the guards became angry and alert. Jurek gave the order that sabotage was to continue, the Germans and Bolsheviks would destory each other while Poland's friends in the west would pick up the pieces with minimum casualities. Then the news came that Finland had come to terms with the Soviet Union, that Chamberlain in England had resigned and the anti-Nazi Churchill was now prime minister and was in Moscow talking to Stalin. An Anglo-Soviet pact was signed with Polish troops in Africa fighting the same enemy as the Red Army. The Polish nationalist position was being redefined. Some weeks after the German invasion some Polish communists arrived at the camp in new green uniform with the traditional four cornered "confederatka" caps. The Polish eagle, minus its royal crown, was their cap badge. Among them was Halina Bednarska, the former governess of the womens' prison in Lvov. She came straight to Agniezka's hut where she was greeted her former prisoner like an old friend. She told of the evacuation of Lvov and how all the machinery from the factories with their workers had been transported to the Urals before the Germans struck.

She had awful stories to tell of mass murder of Jews, of able-bodied Poles and Ukrainians being transported to the Reich as slave labour. The new Armia

Ludowa, the People's Army, led by Comrade Gomulka who had refused evacuation, was fighting the Germans in the forest. A black cloud passed across Agniezka's mind as she remembered why she was in Siberia. However she decided this was a useful time to impart details of the corruption in the camp. She detailed the time the camp commandment gave favours to his mistresses and the observations of the stores sold to the Sibernian hunters. Colonel Bednarska became very angry. She said a bastard who robbed the food of the people, even though prisoners, should be shot, and probably would be.

With the melting of the snow, nature revealed its beauty, lifting Agniezka's heart to the extent that she realized that the inhabitants of the taiga must love it with the same devotion that she had loved her native Poland. The sunshine through the crystal warmed her feelings also. The image of Henryk, with his soft brown eyes and innocent visage, now occupied her thoughts more often than the burning passion for Poland. Then came the camp meeting at which the announcement of the new conditions obtaining because of the Nazi attack on the Soviet Union. The officers under "Jurek" were warned not to attend but Tadeusz and the "Folksingers" agreed among themselves to defy him. The soldiers and the women prisoners were given time off to assure a good attendance. The meeting was addressed by Halina Bednarska who was an accomplished orator. She explained that Polish socialists and nationalists had their differences in the past but now that Poland was completely occupied by the Germans, the Soviet Union was their friend and ally and an era of co-operation should ensue. The Soviet peoples were fighting like tigers to stem the enemy advances and Leningrad and Moscow were being resolutely defended. It has been agreed with the Soviet government and Polish political and trade union organisations to form a Polish fighting force to be called the Kosciusko division. Prisoners of war and political prisoners alike would be released for enlistment in the new force. Weapons, clothing and food would be supplied gratis by the Soviet government and the functions of the new force would be to fight side by side with the Red Army to liberate their homeland and defeat the Nazis with the help of the western powers. Bednarska pointed out that the Red Army was facing three hundred and eighty Nazi divisions while in Africa where the exiled Polish army was also fighting they faced only thirty divisions. Next to address the meeting was a young balding major wearing shaded glasses. He announced himself as Major Jarulszelski, a landowner, a real szlachta, and a regular army officer. He said he was one of the upper classes who realised that things were wrong in pre-war Poland and had to change, with the workers and peasants being given their democratic rights. For this reason he and his brother officers had placed their military skills at the disposal of the Kosciusko division. The meeting finished with the singing of the Polish national anthem.

Tadeusz sent word to Agniezka that he had moved out of the officer's compound to join the Kosciusko division. When Henryk whispered to her that he too should join with her brother she felt a rush of fear.

"No, Henryk! You are a soldier of Poland. You must be content as a prisoner of war. The Russians have taken half of our country. They are still our enemies. You must stay here and obey your officers."

The words stuck in her craw as she said them. She felt ashamed of her disingenuous advice. She realised then that she cared nothing for the false consciousness of which she had been a childish victim. Her true feelings were for the life of Henryk. She felt now that she loved him dearly as a woman, as a sister and even as a mother, though she was much younger than he in years. He was too good, too honest and too naive to survive a war which seemed to chew up men like some infernal machine. As a prisoner he was at least safe and she was close to him. As for her brother she knew he was strong - strong and clever. He always bested the rest of the family in arguments and he was always top of the class at school. She knew he would do well whatever path he chose. He would both keep his honour and survive.

The volunteers for the Kosciusko division, some six hundred men and thirty officers, marched out of the camp singing patriotic songs to board trucks for Irkutsk where they entrained for camp on the river Oka, between Moscow and Riazan. Tadeusz was promoted Major in command of a company of engineers. There was now, for the first time since his capture, a purpose to his life. Gone was the dead hand of Colonel Kot and the generals with their stupid sense of chivalry and superiority. He had been threatened with courtmartial for treason but he reckoned the days of the szlachta were over. One way or another the war would bring about the supremacy of merit. Aaniezka quietly forgot about her sabotage campaign and kept herself close only to Anna and, of course, Henryk whose simplicity and dependence fulfilled her emotionally. She was advised by Halina Bednarska that the Russian camp commander had been courtmartialled for economic crime and shot. Halina was now in charge of all female prisoners. The outcome of her complaint horrified Agniezka but Halina told her that at the front decent men and even boys were dying by the thousand and in the grand scheme of things a scoundrel's death measured very little.

Agniezka began getting letters from Tadeusz whose division had been mustered on the river Oka ready for moving to the Belorussian front where it was destined to spearhead the liberation of Poland and the siege of Berlin. At camp Dzierzinsky some months later a Polish general by the name of Anders arrived at the camp. He went first to the officers and told them an agreement had been made to form a Polish national army under the command of the exiled goverrnment in London. They were to fight on the Russian front alongside the Red Army but they, as officers, had to circumvent this by 'non-cooperation'. He explained to them that there were already Polish forces in the middle east and it was his intention to lead volunteers for the new army out of the Soviet Union and into Palestine where they would join up with the emigre army. The camp quickly became a military establishment with the sound of drill sergeant's bellows backed by the staccato of machine gun fire reverberating round the low Siberian hills. Weeks and months passed by in the military routine but General Anders' men never seemed to be yet fully trained. Eventually the Red army reduced their rations to those of non-combatants and when it dawned on the Red army generals that Anders had no intentions of going to the front they decided to send them to Persia. Persia at that time was jointly occupied by the Red Army and the British Army to safeguard its vital oil from the Nazis.

Agniezka was panic-stricken. She was a sentenced prisoner and not included in the treaty arrangements. Worse still, Henryk would be at the mercy of the horse generals who disregard for casualties was notorious. She decided to confide in Halina Bednarska. Halina was sympathetic; she told Agniezka that without hair she would look like a boy. There were plenty of young soldiers in the camp. A Polish Army uniform would be run up in the stitching hall. Henryk would have to steal a cap, a pair of boots and some buttons from some other soldier.

"I, of course, knew nothing of this, but I will count you present for two days after the army marches out."

Agniezka confided in Anna that she planned to escape with the troops going to Persia. The Gipsy girl's big brown eyes filled with tears as she held Agniezka's hand. She begged Agniezka to take her with her but Agniezka knew that Anna's dark skin would be too conspicuous not to be noticed. Anna had formed a liaison with a Moldovian guard who, while savouring the delights of her little young body, had offered her some tenderness. This had quite a disarming effect on her attitude. He was always advising her to ask for a pardon and apply for Soviet citizenship. This, he said, coupled with a request to do front line duty as a nursing auxiliary, would enable them to be married. An instinctive distrust of any state apparatus lies deep in the psyche of all Gipsies, but Anna, knowing that Agniezka would soon be leaving, acceded to her lover's request. As she had antagonised those prisoners whom she had fleeced at cards she decided she could survive better at the front than in the camp. She was accepted as a recruit for the Red Army nursing service with a promise of a pardon and citizenship for good behaviour. Before the year was out she was to see horrendous bloodshed as the Reichswehr and the Red Army locked horns on the Belorussian plain. By the time the Moldovian had returned from leave with his wife, Anna was staunching bloodflow at the three-week battle at Kursk. There at the most horrific battle of all time, the blood-drenched earth was plowed with burning metal and sewn with the bones of men. For the first time in her chequered life Anna had felt her true worth as she tirelessly worked day and night to tend the wounded and comfort the dying. Later having overcome the German leviathan at Kursk the Red Army fought it's way inch by inch into Poland. There Anna smelt the terrible stench from Mahdenek where one and a half million rotting corpses of Jews, Poles and Russians lay in shallow mass graves, victims of a grotesque nationalist philosophy that judged one race the superior of all others.

Agniezka stood in line with Henryk in the infantry battalion commanded by Colonel Kot. She tried to feel like a soldier by clenching her buttocks under the loose fitting army trousers. The sergeant whom she had smuggled out of Lvov stood at the end of the line but he seemed not to recognise her. Perhaps he did but was fearful she would turn him over to the Russians for what he had done in Lvov. They marched off in columns of four with the kickstart plodding step of the Polish Army. Generals and colonels in immaculate uniform, preserved God knows how, sported their zigzag silver braid which glinted in the Siberian sunshine. Henryk's fellow soldiers, once aboard the train for Teheran and appraised of Agniezka's identity, behaved with perfect decorum as is the nature of the Polish working class. They respected her femininity, her wisdom, he courage and her education. They kept her secret from the officers and N.C.O.'s until the train was safely in Teheran and they had been handed over to the British authorities.

There was a huge military cantonment outside Teheran where the Polish Army was reforming. Regular officers and N.C.O.'s whose careers so far had been as prisoners of war were anxious to get to the Italian front where there was already a Polish force that had seen much action in Africa. They were kitted out in British khaki with Polish insignia and found themselves eating strange English food suplimented by what they could forage from the nearby orange groves and date plantations. Agniezka reported to Colonel Kot that she was the courier from Lvov. His only comment before he assigned her to a clerical job was to state that at least one of her family was a good Pole. Every night she and Henryk trysted in an orange grove half way between their camps. There in the sultry heat of Persia they consummated their love in a very tender way. Agniezka's body developed into womanly curves, her lost adolescence replaced by womanly fulfillment. Her one pre-occupation was to see that Henryk survived the war as all else mattered little to her now. At weekends she would stroll hand in hand with Henryk through the bazaars of Teheran dreaming of some place safe without war where they could have their children. Later when General Anders' Polish Army Corps was moved to the Italian front she always managed to transfer to a unit close to Henryk's.

On the twenty-seventh of July 1944 the first Polish Peoples Army under the command of Marshal Zhukov on the first Belorussian front reached the banks of the Vistula at Demblen near Warsaw. The Koskiusco Division had expanded to take in Poles from all over the Soviet Union. Since crossing the border Polish men of military age were also called up for service. During the drive westward many of the original volunteers from the Oka river camp had been killed or wounded as the Germans had fought like tigers over every inch of land. After a heavy artillery bombardment the Red Army had taken Praga, the Warsaw suburb on the east bank of the Vistula. The Germans had blown the bridge over the Vistula as they left. Tadeusz Jedrusek at twenty-four was now a veteran officer and in command of an engineer regiment that had moved up to prepare for boat and pontoon crossings of the Vistula. His hair was now flecked with grey, the product of fear, bombardment fatigue and the responsibility of five hundred men's lives. His face was bronzed and lean and he looked ten years older than his years. The clear blue Jedrusek eyes still had their sparkle as he scanned the muddy river from his dugout on the bank. Trucks laden with boats and pontoon sections lay hidden in a wood outside the ruins of Praga. Four weeks' fighting without proper food or rest had left him exhausted but now they were regrouping and making preparations to cross the river when an urgent phone call direct from Stalin himself altered the whole situation. The Germans were making a determined counter attack south of the Carrpathians. Ten German divisions of fresh troops were involved in a move that would split the Red Army in two and there was nothing between them and Moscow to stop them if they succeeded. Zhukov ordered General Berling of the first Polish Army to take over the first Belorussian front as the Red Army speeded south.

Three days later a lookout noted strange movements on the opposite bank. The figures appeared to have German pattern helmets but when Tadeusz focused his binoculars he could see the colours of the Polish flag on the side of the stahlhelms. Warsaw erupted in a cacophany of explosions and smallarms fire. General Borkomorowski, Commander in Chief of the Home Army, had started the Warsaw uprising. Tadeusz cursed the stupidity of the horse generals who had sat out the whole campaign without firing a shot and were now jeopardising the first Belorussian front's thinly held lines. They must know that Warsaw bounded by the Vistula was a man-trap for lightly armed troops.

"They would love to lead a cavalry charge down Krakowskie Przedmieski to the old city if only they had a war artist on hand to record it. The horses have more sense than they have."

These remarks were directed to the second-in-command of the regiment, Major Schmuel Blum, who was one of the Jewish officers expelled from the officers' hut at Camp Dzierzinski. He was a decade older than Tadeusz but, in order to stay the mouths of anti-semites, Tadeusz, a practising Catholic, had been promoted over him. Blum was scarred by his rejection by the szlachta and since had interviewed survivors of the Warsaw getto uprising who angrily recounted how the Home army refused to come to their aid in spite of desperate requests for help. All they got from the Home Army's extensive arsenal was a sack containing thirty-nine hand guns. The Cathollic orphanages refused acceptance of Jewish children who had been smuggled out through the sewers unless their parents agreed to their conversion. Major Blum knew also that many hundreds of Jews who managed to make it to the Red Army lines did so only with the help of Poles who would have been summarily executed if caught by the Germans. Blum being more cynical than Tadeusz remarked,

"This is now a soldier's uprising, it is a politican's uprising to seize control of the capital before we get there."

Ten days later the German General Balck moved up the fourth Panzer Army including a division of Russian and Ukrainian fascists. The Germans bombarded buildings without regard to the civilians who were trapped in the city. Soon the Home Army, whose numbers were impressive, were broken up into isolated groups. Requests went out to the Red Army for help via the emigre Polish government in London. Red air force planes parachuted ammunition which didn't fit the Polish Home Army's German weapons. On the eleventh night an exhausted girl swimmer was hauled out of the Vistula by Tadeusz's sentries. She was very tall, about five foot ten, was wearing only green fatigue overalls and was taken to Tadeusz's dugout. After she had recovered sufficiently to talk she told Tadeusz that she was a school teacher and Home Army fighter. As a good swimmer she had volunteered to contact the Russians on the other bank to plead for help. Her long blonde hair was set in wet ringlets round her neck framing a perfectly shaped oval face. This visage of great beauty along with her long slender body moved the normally unemotional Tadeusz. Her blue eyes and kindly smile reminded Tadeusz of his sister Agniezka and as so often happens in these matters she saw in him a family likeness. She was delighted and surprised to find herself among Polish soldiers who wanted to get across the river to help their compatriots. The position of her company was that, with their backs to the river and the boulevard under shell fire, they could not escape. The phone call to General Berling asking for permission to go to the help of the trapped Home Army received a positive response. Tadeusz and the schoolteacher lay together that night in the dugout, both first time lovers. He had never known anyone so beautiful. Maria Taborska gave herself completely to this handsome Polish officer who was wise and decisive beyond his years and who was now going to cross the river to help her comrades. They lay on the camp bed together quietly caressing each other's body before making love again simply and naturally. Both knew they might die before long and both knew that they had at least fulfilment for at least some hours. As Maria slept in the crook of his arms Tadeusz lay awake drinking in the beauty of Maria's exquisite face and form. The next day the regiment prepared the assault boats, checked their weapons and loaded their packs with food, ammunition and spare small arms. At dusk forty assault boats slipped into the Vistula each carrying eight quietly paddling assault engineers. There was still sporadic shooting and shelling on the far bank but as the flotilla got closer a starshell burst over the river illuminating the whole operation. The men paddled furiously hoping to reach the shore before the German artillery could be brought to bear on them. Tadeusz and Maria in the first boat to reach the boulevard scrambled up the steps as the first shells landed in the river sending two boats into the air with crews. The rest of the flotilla paddled upstream to escape the sights of the German gunners. The regiment sustained heavy losses in the crossing, about sixty men were either killed or drowned, weighed down by their heavy equipment. Another seventy sustained wounds before managing to get under cover in the ruined building that the Home Army was defending. The Home Army company was commanded by an elderly lawyer who held the rank of lieutenant. General Borkomorowski was very parsimonious in the granting of promotions, giving his officers only the rank they held when doing their military services which in the case of this man had been during the twenties.

Tadeusz judged the incoming fire as coming from the north, south and west which meant they had their backs to the river with no way out. Communications had broken down so there was no chance to summon assistance from other groups. However they had now plenty of food and ammunition plus three hundred and twenty highly armed and trained regular troops.

After sending out probing patrols with Home Army men who knew the district Tadeusz decided to storm the German positions to the south and head out of the city towards Demblin where the Armia Ludowa had it's headquarters. The elderly Lieutenant had orders to defend Warsaw until the Germans were forced to retreat by the Red Army but, when Tadeusz explained to him there had been no co-ordination with the Red Army which was unlikely to advance again until the battle south of Prague was over, he demurred and the breakout began. The Germans were taken by surprise by the ferocity of the counter attack from the Home Army company being unaware of the presence of the assault engineers from the Army Ludowa. The sappers had planted explosives around the German positions under the cover of darkness. The charges exploded at dawn giving a signal for the Poles to storm the position firing Kalashnikovs from the hip. To their shock and amazement the Poles found they were facing Ukrainian S.S. troops who immediately wanted to surrender. Tadeusz remembered the mass graves of the one and a half million Hews and Slavonic peoples at Majdenek and the part in that crime played by Ukrainian S.S. men and shot them himself as they emerged from their bunkers. On more thoughtful reflection he realised that this summary justice was not altogether fitting; they should have stood trial before the world for their crimes. Later in life he met Paul Jensen a Danish major, who was the only foreign officer to serve with the British S.A.S. regiment. They had done the same thing with the Belsen S.S. guards who surrendered north of Kiel in 1945.

All through this fighting Maria Taborska was at his side firing a Kalashnikov, unafraid and confident and in love. The Armia Ludowa engineers with the Home Army company crossed the Vistula further south without loss to join the head quarters of the first army at Demblin where Maria and Tadeusz were married by Father Krupska, the Kosciusco Division chaplain. Major Schmuel Blum violated all sorts of church dogma by being best man but then Father Krupska was a very liberal priest.

Two more attempts were made by the first Polish Army to cross the Vistula. All were repulsed with heavy casualties. Eventually the situation was resolved as it was in Stalingrad, by crossings north and south of the river, closing the city in a pincer movement. By this time the Germans in their frenzy of destruction had left no two bricks together in the city while the Home Army had surrendered after a month;s fierce resistance. Tadeusz, with Maria by his side as adjutant, fought on to Berlin where sappers from his regiment planted the Polish eagle on the Reichstag.

They stayed on in the army after the war working at the defence ministry in Warsaw. They often saw Schmuel Blum who worked as an architect in the reconstruction of Warsaw until he emigrated to Israel from the pogrom at Kielce where Jewish survivors from Auschwitz were murdered by inflamed superstitious peasants who had believed that the Jews had sacrificed a Catholic infant for the passover. Tadeusz had a phone call from Yitsak Zuckerman, the famous "Antek" from the Jewish resistance, asking for asking for the Jews in Kielce to defend themselves. Without hesitation he instructed the army garrison in Kielce to hand over whatever arms Zuckerman needed.

Agniezka and Henryk were now in Italy with General Anders' Polish army facing the German army opposite the mountain top monastery of Monte Casino. The elite German parachute regiment had turned the monastery into an impregnable fortress and even air force bombers had failed to dislodge them. The British Infantry had failed to dislodge them. Then the Indians tried. Next the New Zealanders nearly succeeded but their government, horrified at the numbers of casualties sustained from such a small population, had them withdrawn. The task then fell to the Poles. Inching their way up the mountain face under withering fire, where dead and wounded men were inaccessible to the medics, they reached a position from which the final assault could be made. An Order group under Colonel Kot sheltered behind a boulder to make the final plans. It included the sergeant, now a lieutenant, whom Agniezka had smuggled out from Lvov. Up behind the massive walls of the monastery a Polish conscript from Katowice in Silesia, now annexed by the third Reich, fired his mortar. The mortar bomb arched over the wall and fell behind the boulder sheltering the O group. Colonel Kot and the entire O group were killed instantly. A lone boyish voice from among the rocks began to sing the patriotic Polish anthem the 'Warsawianka'. Gradually the entire Polish battalion took up the refrain. The last line of the anthem 'Poles fix your bayonets! Long live freedom! Long live Poland! was the ungiven signal for the battalion to storm the summit. The conscript, who had thought he was facing New Zealand troops, knocked his mortar tube to his side tears streaming down his face. He surrendered to Henryk as the charing Poles bayoneted every German paratrooper without his hands in the air.

After the war Agniezka and Henryk went to the Polish Army H.Q. in Scotland where they were demobilised. They decided, or should I say Agniezka decided, to settle in Glasgow where she obtained a loan to start a boarding house and they both prospered and had a family. She maintained contact with her parents in Lvov who were too old to join the exodus to the former German cities of Breslau Posen or Stettin.

Tadeusz was on holiday in Crimea some years later when a dark-skinned lady on the beach heard him speaking Polish to Maria, now the mother of three beautiful and gifted children. She introduced herself as Anna the Gipsy girl who loved Agniezka dearly. When she found out who she was she cried tears of joy to know she was still alive and married to her Henryk. She herself had found her true vocation in nursing and was now a nursing chief in a trade union rest home in Crimea. She had married three husbands, all of whom proved to be, as had the Moldovian guard, moral deliquents of sorts. She was still not above fleecing a patient at cards if she was affronted in some way. Later, as the cold war thawed, the Jedrusek family would assemble in the new restored Warsaw at the, now General, Jedrusek's sumptuous military apartment where their children got to know their cousins. The dark cruel days of the leaving of Lvov were now thankfully long behind them. Both parents cherished wish was for their children to live out their days in the peace that they had so cruelly missed.

Wwladislaw Gomulka, the Lvov trade unionist and resistance leader, later became the General Secretary of the Polish United Workers Party which was a coalition of left wing forces. He became leader of Poland in the late fifties. His foreign secretary did everything in his power to end the cold war through the Rapacki plan but met with no response from the West. Yitsshack

The Leaving of Lvov

Zuckerman, known as 'Antek' the Zionist underground leader, stayed in Poland for two years after the war organising the emigration of Holocaust survivers to Israel. When this job was done he retired to Israel. Major Jaruszelski became Chief of Staff of the Polish Army in the seventies and when the Vatican financed "Solidarinosc" movement threatened to engulf Poland into a conflagration he used the moral authority honour and respect in which the Polish Army is held to restore stability to the country.